Two Hundred Years o

Introduction

This Book is edited from articles written over several years by members of the Foxton Inclined Plane Trust. We hope that the variety of writing styles adds to your enjoyment of the text. Photographs are from our historic collection or taken by various members, specially for this publication.

Visitors to Foxton are often surprised to learn the extent of the country's waterways. Despite the loss of considerable mileage from the system over the years, it is still possible to reach the coast via many different routes and navigate between most of England's major rivers. Whilst the heart of the system survived intact, less profitable routes were closed. Now, however, many of the once derelict waterways have been restored or are under restoration. The canals of Leicestershire remain a vital link in the system. The use of the network generally has changed from freight carriage to pleasure cruising, and the old wharf sites now serve the needs of boater and visitor alike, with Foxton Locks the site of principal interest in the county.

Background History

The development of the Leicestershire canals paralleled that of the rest of the waterway system. In the 17th and 18th centuries, the Rivers Trent and Soar were improved, the navigation eventually reaching Leicester itself. Construction of the Grand Junction Canal began in 1793, between the Thames at London and Braunston, Northants, where it would connect with the North Oxford Canal to Birmingham. It also had a branch to Northampton and the River Nene.

The main canal was constructed to 14ft wide beam. The Northampton arm was narrow, at only 7ft, with 13 locks in 5 miles.

The Leicestershire & Northamptonshire Union Canal was also started in 1793, to connect Leicester with Northampton and the River Nene and struck south from Leicester, via Aylestone, Blaby, Kibworth, and Saddington, where a tunnel was necessary. This gave unexpected problems in its construction, which together with other financial reasons, led to the canal ending prematurely, in 1797, at Debdale near Gumley (just north of Foxton) from where goods were distributed south by road. Debdale remained the terminus during a period of rethinking, after which it was extended with what is now the Harborough arm. The Market Harborough arm was built on a revised route in 1809.

The planned unit of transport on these routes was the 'barge', a vessel up to ... long ... to 14ft wide, as used on the upper Trent, this being more economic than the 7ft wide 'narrowboats'.

In 1810, a new company, the Grand Union (now referred to as the 'Old Grand Union') was formed to build the link from Foxton, on the Leicestershire and Northamptonshire Union Canal, to Norton, on the Grand Junction Canal. They opted for the 7ft gauge for the necessary locks, a factor which was to have major repercussions. The first task was to lift the canal 75ft from the Market Harborough level to the summit section (412ft above sea level) - the '20 mile' - which was to pass through Husbands Bosworth, North Kilworth (with a short branch to Welford), Yelvertoft, and Crick, to Watford Gap, near Daventry. A second set of locks at Watford (Gap) take the canal down 50ft to the level of the Grand Junction.

Foxton was constructed with a unique ten lock staircase with a passing pond in the middle and side ponds adjacent to each lock. Construction along the summit continued simultaneously with Foxton Locks and the two major tunnels, at Husbands Bosworth and Crick. At the Watford end, a mixed flight, of a staircase of four and three single locks, was built to take the canal down to the Grand Junction, at Norton, just south of Braunston. The whole was opened in 1814 - the link between the north, the Midlands coalfields, and London was complete.

The Grand Junction Canal Company

The Grand Junction Canal Company, which owned the main-line canal from London to Birmingham, bought out the Leicestershire and Northamptonshire Union, and the Old Union canals in 1894. GJCCo boundary markers and mile plates, which marked out their property, can still be seen along the canal.

The company set about a programme of improvements. The main restriction to increased trade was the fact that the locks at Foxton and Watford were only 7ft wide, whereas the locks down from the Trent, and up from London were 14ft in width. A wide boat could carry 50 tons, as against 25 tons on a narrowboat, with the same crew and horse. In addition, water supply was a constant headache, with only the three summit reservoirs, and a small one at Saddington.

The answer to all these problems was conceived in 1898 as the construction of an Inclined Plane Boat Lift at Foxton (and another at Watford) which would by-pass the bottleneck of the narrow locks, take the more economic wide boats, speed up traffic by reducing delays, and save valuable water. Fellows Morton & Clayton agreed to put more traffic over the route when the inclines were built. It was a bold and imaginative step, in the best spirit of the Victorian age of technological innovation, and was fostered and promoted by the Grand Junction engineer, Gordon Cale Thomas.

Major refurbishment of the locks was carried out at Foxton in 1927, and date bricks recording them can be seen on the lock walls.

The Grand Union & Nationalisation

The Grand Junction Canal Company was, in turn, taken over with the formation of the (*new*) Grand Union Canal Company in 1929. Other canals had been acquired, and the Grand Union became quite an empire, with assets including sea-going ships and pleasure parks at reservoirs. In the 1930s, as a job creation scheme, an ambitious government programme of improvements to the canal system was put in motion. This was a time of depression, and the roads were starting to monopolise transport.

The locks at Foxton (and Watford) were proposed for widening, and were actually pegged out, with the bottom cottage scheduled for demolition. In the event, the funding did not materialise, and the locks remained as built.

In 1948, most of the canal system was nationalised, and came under the control of what is now British Waterways. By then, the Leicester Line had little traffic and was virtually derelict. A minimum amount of money was spent to keep the waterway (just) operational. The 1968 Transport Act classified canals into three categories: those for Freight use, Cruiseways - to be maintained to a standard for modern pleasure cruising; and Remainder - which would be retained only for water supply or drainage, and not maintained in navigable condition. It was strongly rumoured that the Leicester Line would come into the last category. However, it became a Cruiseway, and this enabled the canal to enjoy a renaissance, in a new role as a leisure amenity. The arm to Welford was designated as remainder and was derelict for many years until it became one of the first canals to be restored with the assistance of volunteers, in this instance, the Old Union Canals Society.

Aylestone Lock, on the Grand Union Leicester Section. All locks north of Leicester to the River Trent were constructed to take a pair of narrowboats, side by side, or a barge up to 14 ft wide. The locks south of Watford (Gap) were also wide, all the way to London. Foxton and Watford were just 7 ft wide.

Midland Waterways

Northwich

R Weaver

Newark

Nottingham

Erewash Canal

Stoke on Trent

Burton on Trent

R Trent

Loughborough

R Soar

Stafford

Trent & Mersey Canal

Leicester

Shropshire Union Canal

Tamworth

Foxton

Peterborough

Coventry Canal

Ashby Canal

Market Harborough

Birmingham

Rugby

Welford

Stourport

Coventry

Wellingborough

R Nene

R Severn

Northampton

Worcester

Stratford on Avon

Grand Union Canal

Stoke Bruerne

R Avon

Banbury

Oxford Canal

Tewkesbury

Oxford

Aylesbury

Berkhamsted

Slough

Reading

LONDON

R Thames

Navigable rivers
Wide canals
Narrow canals
Tunnels

Not to scale

3

Foxton Locks

The construction of the locks at Foxton began in 1810, and they were designed as a staircase flight with side pounds (often referred to as ponds) set alongside. There were ten locks set out in two groups of five with a passing pound between. In this arrangement, the top gates of each lock are also the bottom gates of the next, and the water passes from one lock into the side pound and back into the next lock to equalise the levels. There are other staircase flights on the canal system, of differing designs and operating methods, but Foxton is the longest.

The design, by engineer Benjamin Bevan, is unique in its way of using side pounds to save time and water. Operation is relatively simple and takes an average of 45 minutes to complete, but the fact that boats can only pass each other midway causes a bottleneck sometimes resulting in long delays in times of heavy traffic. When, in 1900, the Inclined Plane boat lift was built to relieve this problem, the size of some of the side pounds and the passing pound were drastically reduced by the earthworks. This resulted in some reduced efficiency in the working and water conservation, which remains to this day.

The Foxton complex took four years to complete and included a cottage at the top and two at the bottom (one of which incorporated an existing building), boat horse stables, a smithy and a carpenters' shop. Foxton bricks were later transported on the new canal, and it is said some were used in London's St. Pancras Station. For the ease of moving materials, a tramway was built next to the works, and when some of the summit canal was complete, cargoes were moved using the tramway. The locks were hardly excavated into the hill since, without mechanical equipment, this was a heavy laborious task. They were built virtually 'on top' of the ground and the earth then built up round them, resulting in them standing proud of the surrounding land and presenting a fine spectacle, both when built and thereafter.

The locks had been in continuous use ever since they opened. Original plans had the Inclined Plane superimposed to partially obliterate the flight, but there must have been a change of mind. During the operating life of the lift (1900 – 1911), the locks were left in disrepair, as all traffic used the much faster lift, and only reverted to the locks when it was closed for maintenance. In 1909, the flight was refurbished for night use. It was pressure from canal carriers Fellows Morton & Clayton for night passage, for their fleet of steamers, which prompted the re-build of the locks. It was not sensible to run the lift at night for a few powered boats. Horse boats usually stopped at night,

*The oldest known picture of the locks **c.**1899. It depicts a grim winter scene as a fully laden family-run horse boat descends the locks. Local boatman William Holloway described the canal as "a bower of wild roses in June and a hell of ice in winter". The locks are in poor repair, and await the opening of the Inclined Plane Boat Lift.*

as the horses needed rest. By 1911, all traffic had reverted to using the locks.

Lock Operation

On a conventional flight of locks, in order to proceed from one lock to the next, it is necessary to have the lock you are in, the canal pound between and the next lock all at the same level. There is no difference between this operation and the locks at Foxton, except that the pounds are located at the side of the locks. The term 'staircase' comes from the format of construction, where the locks are like steps, with the dividing gates on the edge of each step. To negotiate the flight, ground paddles (or sluices) are raised to let water from one lock into the side pound (or pond) and back into the next lock, to equalise the levels. The gates can then be opened, and the boat passes through. Because of this unusual format (there are very few staircase locks on the canal system) the paddles are coded. Those that fill locks are painted red, those that empty are white. It is advisable to raise the red paddle before the white, whether you are working up or down the flight, as this will start to take water from the side pound before any water is put in, so reducing the risk of flooding. Because of this risk, and the fact that, unlike in the days of commercial carrying, boat crews are often unfamiliar with these locks, lock-keepers are usually on duty, to control traffic, and offer advice. They use the little rhyme "Red before white, and you'll be all right; white before red, and you'll wish you were dead!" Using the locks is really a matter of common sense and observation. The schematic diagram, on the next page, shows the flow of the water as the locks are operated. Potential hazards include: something jamming between a boat and the lock wall (there is a clearance of only a few inches); drifting back onto the projecting cill (the ledge on to which the gates close) as the water level drops; getting a bow caught under the lock-gate beam with the water level rising; stepping off into the water. If the boaters just take their time and concentrate, things are not likely to go wrong. There are now more boats using the canals than there were during their commercial hey-day. At busy times, bank holidays and during the summer months, up to 50 boats a day successfully navigate through Foxton flight.

Lock-keepers

At a flight like Foxton, the Canal Company employed lock-keepers, who lived in cottages at the top and bottom. Both had overnight stables attached for the boat-horses. These were spaced at intervals along the canal, and boat crews would make them their stopping places.

A company toll clerk was also in residence to collect the tolls payable on the boats and cargoes. Some families had several generations in the job, notably the Cryers, with Alf the last of these retiring in 1966, the Holylands and the Durrans.

George Durran was lock-keeper from 1929 to 1947, and managed this rather strenuous job despite having one leg and one eye! The day would be filled with essential maintenance work such as greasing paddles, checking water levels, cleaning the stables, cutting grass, and painting lock gates. Going through the locks, the working boatmen knew what they were doing, most having been born to it, so that the job of the lock-keeper - at that time - was one of minimal supervision. They also passed messages between the boat crews, who, always on the move, would welcome news of family and friends. Often a young couple would court with the help of a lock-keeper. The canal was like a linear village, and the "Towpath Telegraph" was (and still is) a very efficient means of communication. The cottage gardens were cultivated with pride, and supplied the family's vegetables, with maybe some over to sell to passing boaters. Nowadays, the locks are managed by seasonal lock-keepers, who do not necessarily live in the cottages. Holiday hirers often need instruction, as do private boaters if they have not encountered these locks before and, at busy times, a system of turns must be established. The numerous visitors ask many questions, but this is nothing new, for Foxton Locks have been attracting visitors since they were first built. Special excursions were arranged by horse and trap from East Langton station, the Cyclists Touring Club made it a destination, and so on. Susan Woolfitt, writing of her World War 2 experiences as a trainee 'boatman', in her book 'Idle Women', said: "The day culminated with a 'Blackpool Pier' effect at the bottom of Foxton, where every type of thing that could float on water was doing so ... the entire hillside was crowded with happy holiday-makers and their picnic baskets, reminding me of Hampstead Heath on a bank holiday".

Where the Water Goes

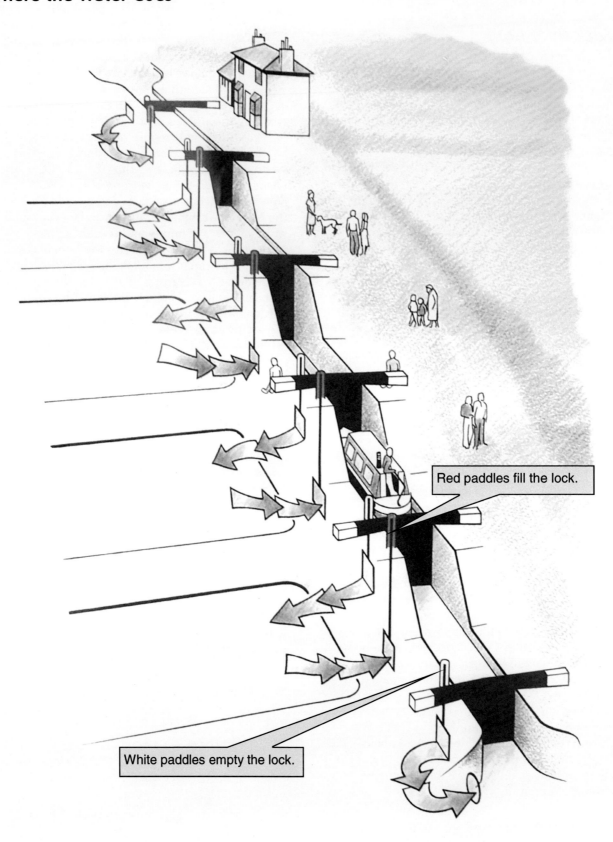

Red paddles fill the lock.

White paddles empty the lock.

Left, The most famous of all the Foxton lock-keepers, George Durran, and Company carpenter Ted Boswell. George was keeper until 1947.
The work flat in the lock is typical of the maintenance boats of the period.

Below, The Cryer family at the bottom lock.

Photos: Alf Cryer

Working life

From the start, the Leicester Line was a through-route joining north and south, with very little industry along the way. The cargo was mainly coal from the Leicestershire, Nottinghamshire and Derbyshire coalfields. As the fuel for steam-powered equipment and domestic use, coal was delivered to all the village wharves, or further south to the London area. Timber was also particularly suited to water transport, and this arrived from places such as Russia, to the ports of Boston and Wisbech, where it was transhipped into narrowboats and made the previously impossible journey into the heart of England. There was a large timber yard at the Market Harborough basin.

These two cargoes were the mainstay and survived into the mid twentieth century. But all manner of other goods were transported by boat, including materials for the Boots drug factory in Nottingham, beer from Burton, bricks, agricultural produce, live animals, limestone for the various waterside kilns, like those at Welford, and Mountsorrel granite. The granite, ironically, was used for chippings to improve the roads, which ultimately put the canals out of business. Some passengers were also carried on a commercial basis, with boats scheduled for market days, and to rendezvous with coaches on the turnpike (old A6). When the railways developed in the 1830s (the Leicester-Swannington Railway opened 1832), this new network had a speed of operation that the canals could not match, and the competition had a detrimental effect on canal trade. The canal companies had to cut their tolls, and some ceased to be viable. However, in many cases there was considerable co-operation between railway and canal, to their mutual advantage. The Grand Junction Canal Company, which took over the Leicester Line in 1894, did a great deal to promote trade on the line, working in conjunction with the firm of Fellows Morton & Clayton, the principal carriers of the day. Perhaps the most significant cargo was rail track and the iron segments to build the London Underground.

The advent of the motor lorry was the death knell for canal transport, particularly after the Second World War, when the road-building programme accelerated and lorries could accommodate ever bigger loads. Coal ceased to be the main fuel of industry, and many pits, which the canals had been built to serve, closed down. By the 1950s, the Leicester Line had no regular trade, and became virtually derelict. The big freeze of 1962/63 saw the canals frozen solid for three months, after which the nationalised British Waterways fleet was disbanded. By 1970, all regular narrowboat carrying had finished. Occasional boats delivered to canal-side property, and a few brave souls have tried to revive canal transport, but with limited success.

As the original purpose of canals diminished, another use gained popularity: pleasure boating. A few of the rich had pleasure boats in the past, but the relative prosperity of ordinary people after the war meant that, for the first time in history, they had leisure time and some money to spend. They got afloat in nearly everything, from Second World War pontoons and old life boats, to cut-down wooden working craft.

By the 1970s, many of the old wharf sites had been rescued from dereliction by becoming boatyards and bases for the holiday hire fleets that were increasing in number throughout the country. At Foxton, the toll-keeper's house, and old carpenters' and blacksmiths' workshops were gradually developed to serve the modern boater, with repair services, a shop and, later, a pub, small hire fleet, and passenger trips for the visitors.

The quality of this rare picture is not good. It is a copy from a very small print taken by one of the lock-keepers when the lift was still in existence. The FMC steamer, Victory, departing Foxton Top, appears to be fully loaded. These boats could only take 12 tons, because of the extra space and weight taken up by boiler and fuel. However by working "fly" (non-stop day and night with crew sleeping in shifts) they could compete with the railways for parcel traffic. The lift can be seen in the background.

Buildings

The Foxton Locks area was typical rolling Leicestershire farmland before the canal came through. First, the length from Debdale to Market Harborough opened in 1809. This swept round in a semi-circle along the contour, through the lands of Sir John Palmer, whose family are still in the county. When, in 1810, the newly-formed Grand Union Canal Company started the final stretch to link the North Midlands coalfields with London, they took a line due south, climbing the high ground with the flight of ten locks. This meant cutting through the cart track between the villages of Foxton and Gumley. This was taken over the bottom lock on what is now Bridge 61; a very rare example of a road-width bridge crossing a lock chamber. Alongside the track was an existing single storey building, possibly a byre, or small, three-roomed cottage. Its frontage would be buried under the built-up bridge ramp, so a second storey was built on, with a door out to the new road level. A toll-clerk was needed, to collect the tolls payable when boats crossed from one company's canal to another. He and his family were now housed in this building, the small upstairs room becoming the toll-office. Downstairs, a lean-to extension was added, and an outside privy and a pigsty. In the back yard, a well, fed from an underground stream, served the buildings and supplied the drinking water for the passing boats, until mains water was installed in 1957.

When the Inclined Plane was opened in 1900, the area changed dramatically. The toll-keeper's job became obsolete when the Grand Junction Canal Company took over the original two canals in 1894, and the cottage was extended again. A two-storey wing was added at right-angles, parallel to the lock, and weather-boarded on the outside (a style unusual in this area). The one large upstairs room was panelled in parana pine, with a marble fireplace and ornate over mantle, as an office and dining room for the directors of the GJCCo, at their now prestige location. Downstairs, a new front door led into the living quarters, with a gridded culvert in front to take the excess water that often flooded down the locks! This cottage is now part of the Foxton Locks Inn.

Opposite, alongside the bottom lock, a lock-keeper's cottage was built, to the standard Grand Union Canal Company two-up, two-down pattern, with central front door, sliding sash windows, slated hip roof and lime-washed walls of local brick: a classic small Georgian vernacular building. However, in this case a third storey was built below the level of the lock side used for the scullery. It is possible that lock cottages were whitened to stand out in the landscape and pin-point the lock sites for the boatmen. Alongside this was a single-storey stable, to accommodate five horses. The stable has been converted to a shop and extended to house the new Bridge 61 pub. At the top lock a similar keeper's cottage and stables were constructed. These have now been refurbished as the Coffee Stop and interpretation space.

It was not clear where everybody was housed when the Incline opened, but at some stage an extension was added to the bottom stable, comprising two small brick-floored rooms, with fireplaces, and a loft above, accessed by a ladder. Too good for a shed, but very basic for a dwelling. The ubiquitous pigsty went on the end. Most country households kept a pig.

At the top of the locks a complete second building appears, almost opposite the cottage, just beyond the top lock. From the available photographs it has the look of a 'signal box'; wooden, or wood-clad, with external steps to an upstairs door. Was it a look-out for traffic up the flight? By 1920 it had vanished and few foundations can be found, giving credence to the notion of a 'temporary', portable, or kit-built structure. Redundant canal buildings were usually adapted for other purposes, or gradually robbed of their materials, for use elsewhere, as was the Incline boiler house.

The projected widening of the locks in the 1930s necessitated demolition of the bottom cottage, and the Holyland family who lived there were given an eviction notice, and moved out. However, the funding did not materialise, and the cottage remains, but considerably extended in the 1980s, to a make a comfortable family home.

By the 1950s the canal was hardly used and all but derelict, and the buildings shabby and in bad repair. When they started to be vandalised, a young enthusiast, Tony Matts took over the bottom house and workshops, and he started up Foxton Boat Services in 1966. The old toll-office became a small shop, the Grand Junction office a tea-room. The workshop continued, and the wood-curing shed was replaced by a covered structure, with a wet-dock constructed over the canal alongside. When visitor numbers grew, the need emerged for a pub, and the 'Bridge 61' was built on in 1980, continuing the line of the original building. New regulations demanding enclosed toilets and high specification kitchens later resulted in the incorporation of the old outhouse and privy into the main building.

The Bottom Lock cottages had only a small back yard so the side pond bank was used as a garden. Vegetables and fruit were grown to supply fresh food, and to supplement the keeper's income. In the centre is the top-storey door to the old toll-office. Pre 1900.

The original 'Bridge 61' pub and boatyard operated by Foxton Boat Services. Picture taken in 2003 before the redevelopment of this area.

Bottom junction c. 1900: the Lift towers over the locks. The Company cottages can be seen on either side of the bottom lock.

Top lock cottage c. 1909: the family gathers in the doorway. Note the bays, and Yorkshire sliding sash windows. A new set of lock gates awaits fitting

When a group of volunteers formed The Foxton Inclined Plane Trust in 1980, only the back wall of the original steam-engine boiler house remained, and this structure was authentically re-built to become the Trust's Museum, opening in 1989.

In 2003, British Waterways started to re-develop the site, demolishing the 1970s life-expired corrugated-iron workshops. The pub area was refurbished and it opened in 2005 as the 'Foxton Locks Inn', part of a new waterside pub partnership of BW and Scottish & Newcastle. The boatyard services, a vital part of the infrastructure of the canal, were re-located a short distance away, and the 'Bridge 61' was re-created, in 2006, adjacent to Hall Brook Cottage on the canal side. The locks site has therefore gradually evolved over the years, and continues to evolve, to meet the prevailing requirements.

Trevor Towers (foreground) and Dave Goodwin lay bricks in the parapet 1988.

The Boiler House under reconstruction c.1986. All of the work was done by volunteers, who also raised money by "selling" bricks for £1. Names were written on the bricks which were then built into the walls, name inwards. For such a young organisation, this was a great achievement and, when completed in 1989, it opened to the public as the Foxton Canal Museum.
From left: Peter Mayes, Trevor Towers, Dave Goodwin, Steve Barfoot, Peter Cook, Mike Beech.

The Inclined Plane

The terms 'Lift' and 'Incline' are often used to mean the same thing, when they are not. 'Lift' implies a vertical ascent via a mechanical contrivance; 'Incline' refers to a slope. Foxton was an Inclined Plane Boat Lift. The word 'Incline' is used as an abbreviation.

Probably the most famous and most published photograph of the lift, taken on 10th July 1900.
A flag is raised on a temporary pole for the official opening. FMC horse boats ascend and descend in pairs while crew and dignitaries watch.

The photograph may well be posed, with the lift stopped at the half way marker.

Exploration

Sifting through modern canal literature one can quickly arrive at a list of 40 lifts and inclines that have existed in this country - a staggering total (*refer to 'Lost Canals & Waterways of Britain' by Ronald Russell*). Similarly, one can easily track down 20 references to patents relating to locks, lifts and planes. This adds up to a wide range of construction and operating methods. Research of a more practical nature, locating old sites on the ground may satisfy only the dedicated. Many have become casualties of modern building schemes or exist only as vague earthworks.

Notable exceptions are the Hay Incline (Ironbridge Gorge Museum), Morwellham (Open Air Museum) and, of course, Foxton Inclined Plane Lift. It is also worth visiting the funicular lifts found at many seaside resorts. A ride on these will give something of the feeling of travelling on the Foxton Incline.

Famous British Sites

By comparing famous British sites, the progression from boat cradles to ever-bigger water tanks can be followed, starting with the underground inclines in the Worsley Mines of the Duke of Bridgewater. If length of run impresses, there was the mighty Morwellham Incline (237ft fall) on the Tavistock Canal, and its rival at Hobbacott Down (225ft) on the Bude. If your yardstick for perfection is longevity, there must have been something eminently practical about the Shrewsbury Canal's Trench Incline, sadly now gone; it lasted 124 years. To an engineer however, the deadweight of the tanks perhaps gives the best clue as to the true sophistication of a design. Foxton is a clear winner here. The Hay Incline, built in the 1790s was at first laid using cast iron tram plates worked with rope haulage. It could only cope with a pair of special tub boats weighing 5-6 tons each. By 1850, the Blackhill Incline was constructed on the Monkland Canal, near Glasgow. This carried boats afloat, but since the all up weight was only some 80 tons, it was meant to take empty boats only. This was the forerunner of the Foxton design.

Foxton

Foxton represents the ultimate in Incline technology in this country. Built at the turn of the 20th century (1898-1900), this best-known site in Britain consisted of a pair of counterbalanced water tanks running on rails on a 1:4 slope. The system was capable of passing two loaded narrowboats up and two down simultaneously. Each tank weighed 240 tons. We had come from the age of the Hay, with cast 'rails', through the era of wrought iron production, to a time and a design when only modern steel would support the weight of the caissons.

1894 Memorandum

The Watford site was compared with this basic design. The seven locks with a fall of 56ft would need a slope 24ft longer, the travel time being increased by one minute. Likewise, Foxton, with its ten locks and 75ft fall, would need an increased slope length of 100ft, and take four minutes longer to negotiate. A time saving of three hours was claimed for passing the summit section, together with "the saving of all lockage water". There were additional calculations determining the power of water turbines being used as the drive (32 hp coming from a 56ft fall - more than enough to do the job). The convenience of oil engines was also discussed. The design was put forward as being 'perfectly practicable' and the building of a working model at a scale of ¼ inch to the foot was proposed - 'with model barges and proportionate tackle'.

A model was built in 1896, and the Chairman's suggestion is minuted that 'an enlarged model be made to further demonstrate the principle'.

The Original Patent

The first step in the story was taken in April 1896 when Barnabas James Thomas, Joseph Jex Taylor, and Gordon Cale Thomas made the original patent application. Of necessity, these papers are couched in pedantic legal language, the sentences never ending! Interesting differences can be spotted when comparing site remains and photographs of the old structures. Tank sides are shown with large radius corner panels, twin sets of double flanged special wheels run on five (not four) pairs of rails. The hauling cables are shown passing around a series of small pulleys set in an arc, rather than around large wheels as in the final design. The earlier concepts were underlined - savings of water and time. The basic form was outlined: transverse tanks carrying boats afloat, the simultaneous passage of tanks in both directions, and a balanced system. There were however major omissions. Work carried out at the company workshops at Bulbourne near Tring produced additional refinements. Company minutes indicate that in October 'the enlarged model' was completed and working satisfactorily.

The Bulbourne Model

When the dates of the various stages are compared, it becomes clear how important the Bulbourne tests were in the development of the Foxton Incline. The experiments warranted sufficient interest to be reported later by 'The Engineer' magazine in a short article with photographs. This describes the model as being 'of full scale as regards the breadth of the caissons and connections with the shore ends of the canals, but is shortened in length, so that the caissons run on only two wheel tracks each, instead of about five, as would be required in the actual fulfilment of the project (note five tracks still, as in the original patent). From the photographs, the depth of the trial tank seems to have been about 5ft (i.e. full size) and the wheels to be about 2ft in diameter. It is clear that the trial plane had a 1:4 (25%) gradient which was suggested in Thomas & Taylor's memorandum, and eventually used at Foxton. 'The Engineer' article includes four photographs taken by H. R. de Salis, showing the model during construction. The first is a general view, the second and third, the eastern caisson with timber framing to represent the upper pound of the canal, and the last shows the shed containing the winding gear, guide pulleys and wire rope at the top of the western incline. The model was working satisfactorily by mid October 1896, and the mechanical engineers Hunter & English were

14

Continues on page 16

The experimental model of the Lift at Bulbourne Herts, with the designers and Grand Junction Canal Company (GJCCo) Directors posing for the camera.
This model was used to prove the design. November 13th 1896

photograph taken by H. R. de Salis

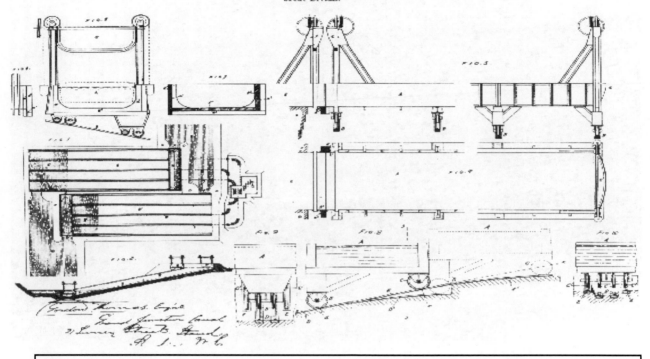

The Thomas' Canal Barge Lift
Grand Junction Canal
Great Britain

Above - Plans which must have been drawn up after the Bulbourne model was produced, as the modifications are included. They are signed by Gordon Thomas from the GJCCo headquarters at 21 Surrey Street, London.

asked to prepare a report. This event has been dated variously as November 1896 and July 1897 - probably preliminary and final reports. The November date is interesting as *'The Engineer'* records that a large party of the leading canal managers and engineers visited Bulbourne and inspected the working of the model on the 13th.

One can imagine Gordon Thomas arranging the visit as soon as he received the favourable report from Hunter & English on the 9th! The idea of gradually diminishing the gradient at the top of the Incline to balance the loss in weight as the lower tank entered the water of the lower canal was not a feature of the original patent, nor was it incorporated in the Bulbourne model. The application for this improvement was registered on 14th November 1896 - the inference is that this modification resulted from the practical tests.

Second Patent

A second, smaller document forms the second patent application, and contains sectioned plans bearing a distinct resemblance to the model. Fresh wording refers to 'a curve of equilibrium' consisting of 'gradually diminishing the gradient at the upper end of the Incline so as to avoid the great increase of haulage power, which would otherwise be required to raise the ascending tank from the moment when the

descending tank begins to enter the water'. One final refinement needed was a duplicate set of wheels on the upper axles, with a secondary set of tracks to pick the tank up and keep it upright. Although the due process of providing the complete specification, and gaining acceptance of the patent, ground on for some time, the final form was down on paper, to be accepted on the 13th November 1897. Gordon Thomas received three tenders 'for machines and steelwork under conditions embodied in a 'specification of terms'. The contract was awarded to J & H Gwynne, because they suggested the use of hydraulic machinery to operate all of the ancillary equipment.

Thomas Letter 12th October 1897

Thomas comments: 'There is no individual specification which appears to embrace the whole of the mechanical conditions to be dealt with; but there are many good points contained in the specification of Messrs Glover and Messrs Gwynne; and it would appear that a combination of certain parts of these two schemes would produce a highly satisfactory machine. For instance the hauling drums proposed by Messrs Glover are without doubt the best system, and these can be applied to the original idea which has been adopted by Messrs Gwynne's viz: one free balance rope and two hauling ropes to each tank. Then Messrs Gwynne's proposal for

16

equalising the strain on each is most satisfactory, as also is their suggestion for actuating the lift up gates by means of hydraulic pressure utilising the engine for pumping up the accumulator'

Costs

Land at Foxton was bought from J Crisp for £1,595 and there were additional surveyors and solicitors fees. Gwynne's quote came in at £14,149 but, with 'other works', escalated to £22,914 (compared with the estimate of £12,000). The grand total, including wages up to the completion date of 24th June 1900, amounted to £39,224.

Gwynne's Pamphlet 1901

Gwynne's Engineering Company Limited traded from their Hammersmith Ironworks between 1849 and 1927; the story thereafter is a dismal one from our point of view. It is a tale of take-overs. During the First World War they produced aircraft engines and then went on to manufacture the 'Albert' car, the engineering of which was ahead of its time. Pumps with the Gwynne name in the casting are still in use.

The transfer of business to various other sites led to the destruction in 1968 of all pre 1927 records. Copies of a 1902 sales brochure produced by Gwynnes are held in the archives at the Leicestershire Records Office and the Waterways Museum, Stoke Bruerne. The pamphlet consists of a four page folder entitled 'Patent Barge Lift, Foxton, Leicestershire'. It contains photos of the upper docks, the Incline faces, the lower docks and the winding machinery. It seems to have been based on Thomas's own figures produced following the first six months working. A transit time of 12 minutes is mentioned and this is compared with one hour and 15 minutes through the locks - one hour 20 minutes to pass a 'pair'. In view of the actual traffic experienced, optimistic official estimates of the Lift's potential were quoted - 6,000 tons moved per 12 hour day, for a cost of £1. 4s. 6d. 'including coal, oil, stores and labour'. Put another way, between 190 and 200 boats could be passed in a day. The actual size of the tanks is given as 80ft by 15ft by 5ft 'capable of carrying two 33 ton canal boats or one barge carrying 70 tons. Virtually all the same information, along with some of the photos, are contained in an 'Engineer' article dated 25th January 1901.

THE 10 H.P. GWYNNE

THE FLEXIBLE CAR—WALKING PACE TO 60 M.P.H. ON TOP GEAR

10 H.P. FABRIC DE LUXE SALOON £285
10 H.P. COACH-BUILT SALOON - £285

It is a car that offers an extraordinary number of advantages, smooth, sweet silent running, roomy and luxurious body, ability to cover long distances at high average speed without fatigue to the occupants, complete and utter reliability; all these, combined with very low upkeep cost—only £10 tax for instance. Among British Cars of fine quality there is no value for money to equal the English made 10 H.P. GWYNNE.

Full particulars with pleasure on request.

10 H.P. GWYNNE DE LUXE 2-SEATER £220
10 H.P. 4-DOOR 4-SEATER - - - £225

During the First World War Gwynnes made aircraft engines. After the war they supplied a similar engine to a car maker. When the car company failed Gwynne made cars themselves, which included those in this advert and the 'Albert'. They also made small fire engines based on the car with a Gwynne pump fitted on the back. One of these and about a dozen cars survive.

Grand Junction Canal Company Personnel

Four personalities dominate the story of the Grand Junction Canal Company (GJCCo) in the East Midlands at the turn of the century - the years of the building of the Foxton Lift. There were regular monthly 'face-to-face' meetings between them to inspect and discuss progress on the works.

Gordon Cale Thomas

Gordon Cale Thomas worked for the GJCCo between 1891 and 1916, and was the engineer in charge of the Lift project. As the Company Engineer he eventually ran the whole GJC empire from their London headquarters at 21 Surrey Street. He was also a partner in the engineering design consultancy 'Thomas & Taylor'.

Right, Gordon Thomas sitting in the balance wheel pit in the bottom basin during construction c.1899.

His shooting stick, panama hat and light coloured suit suggest a prosperous man with a flamboyant personality.

Barnabas James Thomas

Gordon's cousin, answering to 'James', was also a partner in Thomas & Taylor. He was appointed resident engineer for the construction of the Lift.
James appears similar to Gordon in the photographs. Both are wearing the fashionable beard, but Gordon is usually identifiable as the more dapper dresser!

Left, Barnabas Thomas is pictured modelling what is believed to be the uniform for Foxton lift staff.

Thomas William Millner

Thomas William Millner was the manager in charge of the GJC's Northern District from 1896 until his retirement in 1929, which coincided with the Grand Union takeover of the Company. He lived in Canal House, Blisworth, close to the maintenance workshops at the junction with the Northampton branch.

Most of his letter copybooks were rescued by George Freeston of Blisworth and are now held in the Northamptonshire Record Office. Some glass plate negatives of his photography were donated to the Foxton Inclined Plane Trust.

The hardback copybooks were produced at the end of each working day and involved transferring an image of the, usually hand-written, letters to the tissue pages of the copybook, by the careful application of damp blotting paper. This information has helped extensively in the production of this and other Trust publications.

Millner, pictured on his Bradbury motorcycle.

Thomas Holt

Thomas Holt was manager of the Leicester section, based at Kilby Bridge, Wigston. He began his career with the former Grand Union Company, and retired in 1914.

He was closely concerned both with construction and maintenance of the lift, and also with the rebuilding of the locks towards the end of the life of the lift.

Holt, pictured examining a failure in the pulley wheel support bearing. (see page 38 for more details.)

The Lift Operators

John Cryer, Jess Holyland, and Tom Mercer were the three permanent Lift operators. They all lived on site, and came from long established local canal families. The Durran family also lived at the locks for many years, and several members were long-serving employees.

An inspection of the works - two lift operators catch ropes from the boatmen and the GJCCo "big wigs" are on the boat or on the dock.

Grand Junction Plans

The capital works planned by the GJCCo, following their purchase of the Leicestershire Canals in 1894, were extensive. The Foxton Boat Lift was to become the focus of world-wide attention. The company's aim was to speed traffic, save water, and to use wide boats over the route. If the latter aim was to be realised, a tandem project had to be undertaken to upgrade the narrow locks at the Watford end of the summit as well as at Foxton. Although a duplicate lift was under consideration, it is not generally known that several other options were pursued. While Gordon Thomas, as Company Engineer, was personally responsible for the Lift, it was Millner who was delegated to survey Watford Locks, with several alternative schemes in mind.

At the time the Watford lock chambers were in a sad state of dereliction. One contemporary writer referred to them by saying: *"Such a tumble-up set out I never did see in all my born days. To take 20 tons .... through eleven creaky old lock gates and rotten paddles was a work not to be laughed at"*.

Some of the lock walls had bulged so badly that boats had to use block and tackle to get through. Straightforward rebuilding would not accommodate bigger boats and it seems the idea of simply widening the locks to 14ft was not what the company had in mind either.

In December 1895 Millner submitted a rough plan and sections for "three 18ft Lift Locks" and, three months later, another scheme which suggested four chambers, each of which would have been approximately 14ft. deep. There was no mention of back pumping in all of this, so it seems to have been to ensure the Main Line summit (at the foot of the Watford Flight) was supplied with extra water. It is obvious that, in 1895/6, the projected Foxton Lift (still at the patent stage), alterations at Watford, and back pumping at Braunston were considered as part of one massive inter-related plan.

While the pump went ahead in 1897, and the Lift was built between 1898-1900, the company played 'wait and see' and a decision on Watford was deferred. So much depended on additional traffic making all this effort worthwhile. Millner must have been disappointed that his 'Cinderella' schemes were destined never to see the light of day. In 1902, the idea of a second boat lift, and the use of wide craft was finally abandoned. The extra traffic promised by Fellows Morton & Clayton had not materialised, and steam-powered narrowboats, capable of towing one or more conventional horse boats, were gaining in popularity. The narrow Watford Locks were simply rebuilt.

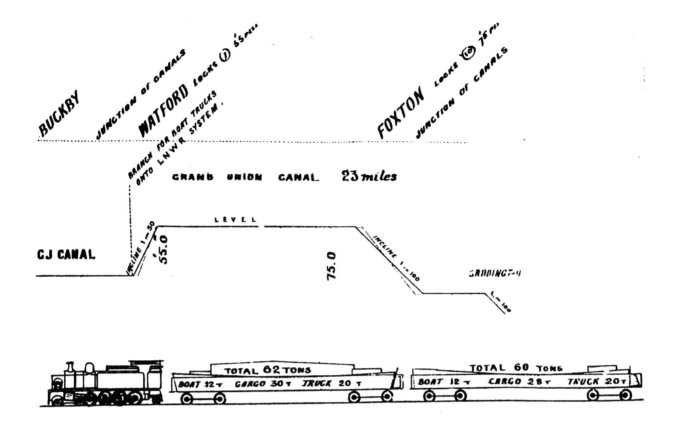

Bertram William Cook's Plan

This shows how the Leicester Line almost became a railway! He didn't say how he would negotiate the Foxton rise in any detail, save to say it would consist of a 1:100 incline (and presumably a long deviation across new ground to achieve the drop). The average train would consist of four narrowboats carried on bogie wagons. Think of the stress on a loaded wooden hull! His plans almost amounted to disloyalty, and he subsequently left the Grand Junction Canal Company for America. Perhaps he made good in a land that was more eager to foster radical ideas?

FOOTNOTE

The American Allegheny Portage Railroad and Canal system was constructed in 1831-35, from Philadelphia to Pittsburgh, a combined canal / railroad route of 280 miles with a central Incline section 36 miles long.

Coils of steel being loaded at Leicester's Belgrave Wharf in 1956. The cargo was destined for Spain via London docks. Butty boat Oxted is being loaded and motor Brighton and an unidentified motor wait their turn.
The Pickfords name on the crane is a reminder that Pickfords road transport started out as a canal carrier.
The site is now part of Leicester University.

The Inclined Plane Construction

Geology of the Area & Excavations

The Lift is situated in a clay area on the boundary between the base of the Middle Lias and the Lower Lias deposits. The line of the canal through Foxton village towards Market Harborough runs above the characteristic change of slope and 'spring-line' between the two deposits on the valley side. Drainage is to the River Welland.

When fresh excavations are exposed to wet weather, the clay is easily turned into deep mud. Frost and the action of running water will quickly erode unprotected cutting and bank faces into deep gullies, and the failure of embankments can be sudden and catastrophic, involving massive amounts of material. Earthworks using local soils are subject to considerable settlement. All these were problems the Victorian engineers had to overcome.

Earthworks Construction

The banks were stabilised by deliberate planting (there are mature larches on site), facing some parts of the embankments by building revetment walls and improving run off by incorporating 'burnt clay' (a clay/coal mixture, burnt on site, resulting in a gravelly 'crust' not unlike brick rubble). Put simply, in the construction of the Foxton Plane, clay excavated from the bottom docks area provided material for the top part of the slopes and the upper canal approach. The banking was raised in 'benches', this construction giving more stability.

The point has been made that more use could have been made of the natural slope of the ground - approximately 1:10, and it is certainly curious how the earthworks encroached upon the line of the side pounds serving the lock flight. This resulted in the pounds being much reduced in capacity, particularly the meeting pound and above.

Patent plans demonstrate that alternative layouts were possible. In principle, the planes did not have to be adjacent as they were built. There are many factors which could have affected the final design: minimising land purchase, giving better approach to existing waterways etc. The location of the lift was fixed by the summit and the lock flight, and the gradient of the slope, at 1:4, was perhaps fixed by mechanical considerations.

A vertical lift would still need approach canals sitting on very substantial embankments. A shallower incline would need longer track-work and hauling-cable runs. The question of orientation was perhaps more a matter of solving the difficult earthmoving 'balance' by making the excavated material from the cuttings match the volume needed for banking.

Equipment

Early photographs show the sequence of construction and the equipment used. The ground was dug by hand, with planked 'barrow runs' well in evidence and the items of 'Jubilee' construction railway (20" gauge) and their tipper trucks can clearly be seen. The trucks were manufactured by Howards of Bedford, agricultural engineers with a world-wide reputation. Their design was somewhat crude, with axles turning in cast-iron blocks with no proper bearings or latch mechanism to hold the bodies upright. The hoppers were fitted with lifting loops and 'feet', which would have enabled them to be de-mounted, and used on site in a similar way to a modern rubbish skip (see exhibits on site at Foxton Locks).

On level ground, these trucks would have been pushed by men or horse hauled. Track laid diagonally across the part completed planes, and later directly up the 1:4 was operated with a cable and portable steam engine. There are references in company minutes to three 'hoisting engines' and a 'concrete mixer' being bought, and several sheerleg-type cranes were erected to move the heavier items of plant.

Rail Foundations

Site investigation has revealed that the track of the Incline was supported on concrete foundations poured in 18" 'lifts'. In the upper part of the hill these foundations reach down 25-30ft, to sit on the under-lying rock, with a line of piers and arches beneath each pair of rails. These were tied together with fabricated steel ducts, which ran laterally across the planes at intervals. Other important items were tied back to this web of structure work. The earth infill was incidental to the strength of the main construction, and the whole surface was topped with a layer of granite flakes.

The Rails

The track used was not of a modern type with 'chairs' and lateral sleepers. It employed 'bridge-rail' pinned directly to longitudinal baulks of timber - Brunel's old broad gauge Great Western Railway pattern. On the incline, various items of the old rail system have been discovered - timbers, bolts, joining plates, all closely following the GWR pattern. Comparisons between ex-GWR rail (displayed at Foxton) and remaining timber baulks indicate that Gordon Thomas had new rail rolled, though plenty of the former railway metals would have existed at the time. Only a few short lengths of original Incline rail have survived demolition, but from this Trust members have been able to research the history of the Lift's rails. Luckily, the name 'Dowlais' appears on the old section of rail, giving the clue to its origins. There were many famous names associated with the Dowlais Ironmasters of South Wales. Trevithick experimented with early locomotives in 1804, which ran on the Penydarren Tram road, built by Dowlais men. Brunel had them roll experimental bridge rail, and Henry Bessemer granted the firm patents to roll steel which they refined using his famous steel making process. Several lengths have been assembled on the Incline to give the visitor some idea of its original appearance. Interestingly, these came from the turf sided locks on the Kennet and Avon Canal, where they had been used as fendering. Along the Northern Stratford Canal, there are examples of bridge rail used as boundary markers, fencing posts etc. Both canals were owned at one time by the GWR.

Track Problems

The track, when new, would not lay flat. The ends curled upwards and were pulled down by the bolts. It has been said that the Lift rails gave some trouble in use 'curling up under pressure like a spring'. This fault could have been caused by soft supporting timbers allowing the holding bolts to pull out, the problem made worse by the fact that the tank wheels had no suspension as such. The timber sleepers were changed for a harder wood, and some through bolts seem to have been added. However, engineering problems were never mentioned by the company as a reason for the Lift's closure.

Materials

If materials were not available in the immediate area, they were brought in by boat along neighbouring waterways. Derbyshire freestone was used to replace the ageing local red bricks as the coping of the Foxton lock flight, and Mountsorrel granite (Granodiorite) was used as aggregate for the Lift concrete, revetment walls and surfacing on the slopes.

Workers start cutting the bottom dock. A "Jubilee" rail system in the foreground illustrates the quality of earth moving equipment available. Large numbers of men were employed to dig the foundations. Up to 300 men worked on site.

23

Bottom Dock nearing completion. A dam keeps the canal from flowing into the works. The construction under the bridge is a loading pier for the 'Jubilee' narrow gauge rail system. From this point materials needed anywhere on site could be loaded into a tipper truck and moved by horse or man power. A steam winch was provided to move the trucks up the Inclined Plane. It is easy to move the tracks to a new location.

Remains

The remains on the Lift site show the materials used by the GJCCo. Blue bricks with stone copings for the upper docks, red bricks for the aqueduct foundation piers across the plane top, and more of the same for boiler house construction. There are also bricks for special applications - brown and white glazed bricks for the inside of the boiler room, refractory bricks (from Stourbridge) lined the chimney, and blocks of similar material (from Reading) were used to form the boiler flues. Materials were 'robbed' at various times. The chimney was felled and the bricks re-used for canal repair work. The end walls of the boiler house were still standing until the 50s, when they suffered a similar fate.

Boiler and Engine House

Although most of the original building had disappeared, it was still possible to view the site and, with the help of old photographs and drawings, determine the function of the surviving remains. Visits paid to the Braunston pump house, built by the GJCCo in 1897, just before construction at Foxton began, have also helped. This structure contains many of the Foxton features. Clearly there was a company pattern.

Looking at the Foxton Boiler House - now the Museum - from the locks, the walled space to the right was the coal store. Coal would have been tipped from the loaded boats above, down chutes, and stored in the open. It would have been barrowed inside through the double doors, and into the operating area with its concrete floor and glazed brick walls. A pair of Lancashire type boilers occupied half of the floor area - one in use, one as standby and to enable maintenance to be carried out. An elevated floor level covered these, with access to the plane top, engine, and winding gear via a metal staircase.

The engine and details of the hydraulics are given in old leaflets. 'The engine for driving the main hauling drums working the plant is of the double cylinder high pressure jet condensing type, the power being transmitted to the drums by means of powerful worm gearing. The hydraulic pressure is obtained from a horizontal duplex pump, having outside bucket plungers. This pump delivers into an accumulator, which is sufficiently large to hold a reserve of water to work all necessary cylinders simultaneously".

The tiny tunnels set in the rear wall are connected by a cross gallery, and in the roof of this are set the bolts and retaining plates for the worm gear mountings above. Smoke from the boilers was conducted through a large brick-vaulted flue to the chimney itself, the base of which can still be seen, complete with lightning conductor. There were numerous wells in the floor, the largest of these associated with the accumulator tower, which provided hydraulic power for the operation of the Lift services. With all of this information as a start point, the FIPT were able to reconstruct the boiler house, and open it as a museum in 1989.

The outward appearance of the boiler house was of a fort-like structure with a flat roof. This impression is emphasised by the decorative frieze in blue bricks around the upper courses. Large arched windows picked out heavily with accompanying masonry add to the effect. A round window in the same pattern is set in the end wall above the flue. The original windows of the building were taken to Tring to be used again when rebuilding work was done there. The replacement windows in the reconstructed boiler house came from the Husbands Bosworth Baptist Chapel. Mrs Daisy Dainty (one of the people asked to open the new building) had helped raise money for the chapel when she was a child, and she recalled that her family had moved house taking their furniture down the Inclined Plane.

Perhaps it is the finer details which can be just as interesting as major items. At night, lighting would have been by paraffin lamps, and if the Braunston building can be taken as similar, then that round window would have been operated by a loop of light chain wound round a wooden cleat on the wall to keep it open. Cast-iron rain gutter collecting-heads would carry castellated decoration echoing the fancy exterior brickwork, the GJCCo legend appearing on manhole lids.

The steam engine sat on stone foundation blocks that can be viewed at the upper Incline level, the additional blocks supporting the huge winding drum and hauling cables. The engine house containing this machinery was a wood and glass structure akin to a railway signal box. It has been speculated that large items like the boilers would have posed a problem in their transportation to site, and may have been delivered by canal.

Above. The winding gear, basically "off the shelf" mine winding gear. The engine is on the right. Some early pictures show a wide flywheel, which must have been replaced by this slim version, which could also be used to turn the gear with a long bar.

Left. The engine during installation. It is being lowered onto a timber trackway so that it can be slid into position. It is a vertical twin cylinder jet condensing unit. The drive flange can be seen on the left. The man on the right holds a carpenter's rule, and the lad was possibly an apprentice.

The boiler house and engine room viewed from the locks in 1924.   Photo: Alf Cryer

Incline Top

The visitor to the Incline top often has some difficulty relating the remains of the upper docks to the summit canal, until it is pointed out that they really *are* at the same elevation as the top lock, and that the upper canal approach joins the main waterway halfway between the top lock and Gumley Road Bridge (Bridge 60). Similarly, there is often confusion about the exact method of operation, since the main elements - the tanks - are missing. A brief resume of the basic facts; that the boats were carried, still afloat, in one of a pair of tanks set laterally on the hill, makes things clearer. The difference in heights between the upper docks and the tail head levels was made up by the wheel assemblies beneath the tanks themselves. The two tanks balanced each other, the planes separated from each other in the way they are because they had to be spaced apart by just the width of the docks.

A steel aqueduct reached across to serve the second plane - another major feature removed by the demolition team.

Tanks

The tanks were constructed of steel plates, riveted together, and large enough to take one wide boat or two narrowboats at once. Full-length narrowboats measure 72ft by 7ft, but more room would be needed for the gate assemblies at each end. The tanks were 80ft by 15ft by 5ft deep.

When operational, they would carry approximately 150 tons of water, the all up weight correspondingly greater because of their own structure - another 70 tons. They worked on the Archimedes principle - a boat displaced its own weight of water as it entered the tanks, so it was of no consequence if one tank contained a loaded boat and the other an empty or smaller one, or indeed no traffic at all. The effective weight of the loaded tanks remained constant. As the tanks balanced each other, the engine merely had to overcome the friction in the system, and was used to control the descent. There would have been variables in the system - the cable as it was paid out would progressively increase the weight of the descending tank, changing by some 4 tons. Water levels on the summit and at the lower level could also affect the operation, a difference of 6" amounting to approximately 16 tons.

The Grand Junction staff would have prided themselves on keeping levels 'on weir' at all times, but periods of drought must have brought unique problems for the lift operators.

Left. The winding house is nearly complete and the 'iron trough' aqueduct is in place.

Refinements

The model tests at Bulbourne (reported on page 14) had produced important additional work which had to be carried out for the final design. The tanks were supported on un-sprung bogies running on four pairs of rails up the 1:4 slope. As the lower tank entered the water of the bottom docks, it became effectively 'lighter' and the resistance of the water would have a similar effect. To counteract this the upper ends of the rails were curved on a gentle radius to allow the tanks to run over the crest of the hill, making it easier. In reality, the calculation was done so that the design of the upper curves exactly matched the effects of immersion, and no additional load was placed on the hauling system, or sudden extra surge of power needed from the engine to 'dock' the tanks. This change required another refinement to previous plans - without special provisions the tanks would tilt from the vertical as they approached the upper limits. Secondary rails were laid over the upper curved section outside the main running rails, in an elevated profile. Another pair of wheels (each leading axle was thus fitted with four wheels) ran on to the higher profile, again designed to match exactly the upper curve and keep the tank plumb as it docked.

Above, Gordon Thomas and his wife survey the bogies set out at the start of tank construction.

Below, Gordon Thomas peers out from the lower front leg of a tank, his shooting stick leans on the wheel below him.

Above, the tank is assembled under the watchful eye of Gordon Thomas (far right). It had been assembled with bolts in Hammersmith, dismantled and shipped as a giant Meccano set. Once assembled the tanks were hot riveted. In many of the descriptions of the lift the term caisson was used - this is French for tank.

Construction

The labour force comprised mainly travelling 'navvies' who were housed in huts in the field at the bottom level (which was part of the land purchase), or lodged in the surrounding villages. Some even walked the three miles from Market Harborough each day. The tanks were fabricated on the planes themselves, at the point where they would have passed each other when in use. It is not clear why this particular spot was chosen, rather than say halfway up their respective runs. It may have made access for materials easier from the field at this point, and between the two tanks themselves. Materials handling would have been awkward wherever they were assembled.

A sizeable storage area was established with the workmen's huts in the field. This special position occupied by the tanks under construction was obviously of some importance as it was marked by a register post positioned at the spot. Again, the true purpose of this can only be conjecture, but it must have related to the initial setting up procedure needed to attach, tension and check the hauling cables. The reason why the tanks were constructed on the inclines was probably so that cables could be hooked up and tensioned with the tanks either chocked or balancing each other at all times. They were even left in this position between disuse and demolition.

Cables

There were two hauling cables to each tank connected to the main drum, and a third, central, 'balance rope' linking the tanks in a complete loop around the installation. The purpose of this rope was to ensure that the upper tank would start down, and not hang up in the dock, and it also provided a back-up safety element in the event of failure of the main cables. The cables themselves were 2 ¼" in diameter, having a rather coarse multi-stranded appearance. Although there was provision for some mechanical adjustment at their anchor points, hydraulic cylinders were interposed in the cables. These were in turn linked hydraulically, and a system of check valves gave control over the setting up, and the ability to tension all cables evenly.

Pulleys

The cables passed over numerous rollers set in the face of the plane at intervals to prevent them dragging on the ground. A reconstruction of one can be seen on the Incline top. These could not have been totally successful, as rope marks are to be found on the concrete aprons in the upper rail area.

Larger pulleys guided the cables on to the main spoked wheels, 10 feet in diameter. There were eight of the latter, dispersed across the Incline top, and two at the bottom, one of which is now on display.

Bearings

The bearings for these large pulleys were suitably massive. The top consisted of cast iron pedestals, 2-3ft tall, bolted down to concrete foundations. The lower bearing housings take the form of cast tubes 6ft long, again set vertically in concrete and buried below present ground level. The scene in working days would have looked very different to the present somewhat bare appearance, with cables at various heights crisscrossing the Incline top and disappearing through slots in the walls of the engine house and on to the hauling drum.

The pulleys and their bearings can be seen clearly on this shot of construction at the top of the incline. The small building on the left is the upper part of the hydraulic accumulator tower.

The iron trough aqueduct under construction. (This is seen to the right of the photograph above.)

Above, in the foreground is one of the wheel bearings. In the background Thomas discusses the installation of the winding gear.

Below, construction is nearly complete. One of the tanks sits in the bottom dock with its gates raised for some finishing work. The sheds are accommodation, stores etc for the construction works. To the left of the huts is a jumble of materials and equipment used in construction.

Hydraulic System

The hydraulic system, pressurised by a horizontal duplex pump and accumulator, provided the power to raise the Lift's guillotine gates and work the tank sealing rams, which held the tanks against the dock faces. There were gates in the ends of the tanks, and the two upper docks - six in all. None was needed at the bottom dock where the tanks slipped into the water of the lower basins. The capacity of the pump was 20 gallons per minute, and that of the hydraulic accumulator that it served, about 37 gallons. Recharge (by pumping in hydraulic fluid under pressure to raise a ballast weight in the accumulator tower) could have occurred in approximately two minutes, and been achieved automatically. The operating pressure of the water and anti-freeze hydraulics was in the region of 750 psi.

The following was written using reminiscences, detailed inspection of old photographs, and observations of similar machinery elsewhere. Although the Lift works were scrapped so long ago, fresh details of its operation are constantly becoming known from all these sources.

"The piece of 'machinery' *(illustrated below)* shows the group of three hand levers, which would have been found inside the upper control cabins. Close examination reveals they were mechanically linked, making it necessary to operate them in sequence. 'RAMS' presumably gave control of the jacking of the Lift tanks into the dock face - the first manoeuvre. 'CONDUIT', one can only guess, operated the upper dock gates (at the same time pressurising the hydraulic feed to the lower cabins?) - the second manoeuvre. 'TANK' controlled a more complicated operation involving the manual coupling of the hydraulic pipe connection to the tank gates, an operation imitated at the bottom.

Hydraulic connection - from close examination of the original photograph, it seems the joint was effected via a coarse threaded screw, which projected through to the outside of the control cabin. Operation of the 'TANK' lever simultaneously slid a cylindrical shield over the coupling - implying that it leaked under pressure. This was the last operation in the sequence, and it can be imagined that the levers can only be returned easily to their start positions, that is with all gates down and rams withdrawn, by once again moving them one at a time.

The hydraulic system used at Foxton was water and antifreeze, rather than using one of the many specialist oils which have been developed since. The problems of corrosion, leaks, and frost protection are all much better catered for in our modern age. From their bulk, the old hand valves and cylinders seem to indicate a low pressure, high flow system, and it is known from the specification of the accumulator machinery that pressure was not continuously maintained. The cluster of three lever valves were set on a brick pedestal approximately 2'6" long. If one stood in the doorway of the upper cabins, looking down the run of the Incline, the hand levers would have been at waist height in front of the operator, the telegraph equally close to hand on the left.

Gates

Like the main structure, the gates were manufactured by J. & H. Gwynne of Hammersmith. The riveted lattice frames carried vertically rising gates, which would seal off the tank ends in transit.

They were manufactured and tested as separate units in Gwynne's works by the Thames, shipped to Foxton in knock-down form, and reassembled on site. Roughly painted initials and an accompanying number seen in some of the construction photographs are the clue here. The gates were opened and closed by a series of chains running over pulleys and connected to a ram. The seal between the tanks and the docks (as opposed to between the gates and the tank- or canal-sides) was also controlled hydraulically. Tanks in the upper position came to rest between a 'buffer stop' at one end and the dock face at the other. Rams pushed the whole thing across the last fraction of an inch necessary to seat against the dock. The free play on the axles would be sufficient to accomplish this manoeuvre.

The hydraulic stanchion with connection for the gates on the tanks, seen before it was enclosed in a control cabin.

Services

The site was served by a network of water and antifreeze hydraulic pipe runs, parts of which can still be traced today. The tank gates had to be connected to this system at the top and the bottom, so four control cabins were erected to house the gear. These were suitably positioned in the docks. Again, remains can be traced. The steam engine provided the power for this system, raising a ballast weight in the accumulator tower. The weight could supply the hydraulic services for one complete cycle of operations during its descent, and similar installations can still be found in industrial property dating from the Lift era.

The inclined Plane ~ operation

To understand the method of working it is perhaps appropriate to try to follow an imaginary journey through the Lift. Not on one of those rare days when the Directors' inspection launch paid a visit and everything had to be 'just so', or even on one of those happy occasions when a working boat would be scrubbed out to provide transport for a Sunday school treat, but just an ordinary day when one of the many horse drawn coal boats made its passage.

Approaching beneath the wide arch of the bottom dock bridge, the boatman would see the Lift tank for the first time, thankful that one was down with the guillotine still raised following the exit of the previous boat. As he drifted into position, the gate was lowered behind him, mooring ropes made fast to the bollards, and the horse led away. A uniformed attendant broke the hydraulic connection, ducked into his cabin, and signalled over the telegraph to his colleague in the winding house above. A pause; then movement, very slow at first.

As the tank rose from the canal, the motion created a standing wave, which ran across the bottom dock, lapping on the slope. Water poured from the recesses in the wheel assemblies and dripped from the structure work, to be caught in a series of catch pits cut across the toe of the incline and in special gutters at either side. As it left the lower docks, and started the long climb, small fish would occasionally be stranded and carried aloft.

Compared with 'waiting turns' at the locks, and toiling up the hill for the best part of an hour, the smooth ride up the Lift was completed in twelve minutes. There was time to relax and contemplate the splendid view of the surrounding countryside from this new vantage point. Nearing the top, progress would seem to slacken as the tank rolled slowly over the crest. From the boat, looking back down the hill, the feeling was similar to crossing an aqueduct. At Foxton, though, the unique sideways movement

heightened this sensation, rivalling perhaps gliding over mighty Pontcysyllte! Imagine the effect on an excited party of schoolchildren, but our boatman would have seen it all before.

The Lift operator would control the docking as the rear wheels slipped into their pit and the leading wheel flanges nudged into the timber stops, finally coming to rest. The 'buffer-stop' rams were engaged, pushing the tank imperceptibly into contact with the dock. Another attendant wound a hand wheel, controlling a valve set in the dock gate, and the space between the end gates quickly flooded. With the hydraulics reconnected to the gate cylinders on the tank, both sets were raised.

The horse, having plodded up the path round the site, led by a boy, was hitched up, the line tightening as it leaned into the collar, legs braced, to start the boat out of the Lift entrances. Drips from the raised gates would spatter on the side cloths, the steerer stepping forward slightly at the last moment to minimise their effect as they reached him. The boat was on its journey once more, out across the 'twenty mile'.

Accidents

There were two accidents during construction - minutes report a fatal accident on 5th December 1898. George Robinson, one of the navvies employed on the construction, was killed 'by a fall of earth'. Thomas attended the inquest when a verdict of 'Accidental Death' was returned. It is said that the accident involved one of the tipper-trucks, and these items of plant were certainly the cause of a lesser incident earlier in the year.

Through the Market Harborough solicitor Mr J H. Douglas, George Sharman applied for compensation under the newly passed Workmen's Compensation Act (of 1897) 'for injury caused to his finger whilst engaged tipping wagons on the 8th November at Foxton Lift works'. It is a comment on the times that the Company paid five guineas compensation to the worker, two guineas Doctor's charges, and one guinea Solicitor's costs!

There was one failure of the hauling system, and the scene was captured in a photograph. One of the main hauling pulleys had been lifted from its bearing, the cable lying slack alongside. Half of the upper bearing cap appears to have fractured, the broken section standing nearby. Possible explanations are a little involved. Of the eight main pulley wheels on the incline top, two had cable wound around 180 degrees of their periphery, others only 90 degrees. Those having the cables wrapped around them would carry a higher load than the others. Marks on the timber stops at the top of the incline run show that the tank wheels were powered into them on occasions. A likely cause of

Above, a pair of boats crammed full of people on an outing c.1905.
Today, health and safety controls severely restrict the numbers allowed on trip boats, but these are crammed full of people obviously enjoying themselves.
Water can be seen leaking from the end gate of the tank.

The Lift sits proudly on the top of the hill and chickens are pecking on the towpath near the bottom lock.

The bank supporting the lift still looks bare and raw.

This opening day picture shows a pair of FMC horse boats Marsworth and Langley, entering the top dock, while the dignitaries look on. When the gates are opened, they would drip for quite some time, leaving muddy spots along the boats and soaking unwary boatmen.

Thomas Holt examines the damaged pulley bearing. This photograph is the only record of the incident, as it doesn't appear to be mentioned in company minutes. How it happened is therefore conjecture.

failure, therefore, since the pulley concerned was one of the special pair, was that the tank was overdriven on its run and stressed the system. The balance rope would have prevented a disaster involving a runaway tank. Alternatively, the breakage could have been caused by the pulley seizing on the axle, which forced the key to turn and burst the pedestal.

In 1909, the Company minutes stated that, 'during the recent frost', the hydraulic installation of the Foxton Lift became frozen and five cylinders operating the portcullis gates were fractured, the damage being due to an insufficient quantity of glycerine being mixed with the water used for the hydraulic circulation.

The committee gave instructions for 'two new cylinders to be obtained forthwith, and if it is found necessary to replace the other three cylinders, a further report to be made to the committee'. The Engineer was also instructed to censure the man in charge of the Lift for not carrying out his instructions, and that printed instructions should be posted in a conspicuous place in the engine room 'with a view to preventing a similar accident occurring in the future'.

Steam

In 1897, the Grand Junction Canal Company completely rebuilt the Braunston Pump House, which was designed to pump back the lockage water otherwise lost to the Oxford Canal. An old illustration **(page 41)** shows the layout, similar in many respects to that at Foxton, where work on the Lift project started the following year. The Braunston installation relied on a single Lancashire boiler, as opposed to a pair at Foxton. From old correspondence the new centrifugal pump and steam engine were supplied by the same makers.

As at Foxton the boiler room machinery has been installed before the building is constructed, window frames are set ready for the bricklayers to build around. The steam engine (similar to Foxton's) was supplied by the same makers - Gwynnes of Hammersmith. Any letters referring to Foxton directly have tantalisingly yet to come to light. It may be that Gordon Thomas dealt with Lift matters personally, rather than have it passed through his second in command. However, Braunston is so similar and close in time that piecing together its story gives a very real insight into events likely to have taken place on our own site in Leicestershire. Work at Braunston settled into a pattern, reports going directly to T.W. Millner at Blisworth. A regular check was kept on boat movements, the state of Daventry Reservoir, and the canal depth across the Braunston/Buckby Summit. This constant stream of data arrived by telegram and letter addressed to Millner's office.

The Foxton hierarchy was a little different, with the Lift crew probably reporting to Thomas Holt, the Area Engineer at Kilby Bridge. Holt held regular meetings with Millner to discuss work on the Leicester Section, but there are unfortunately infrequent direct references to the Lift itself. Holt's correspondence centred more on the weather, Foxton/Watford Summit levels, and

1905 maintenance. Three men are renewing the gate seals, the gate being tied back to the plank set across the tank. A dredging boat and ice breaker are being used as maintenance boats. Trees and bushes are sprouting on the banks. Part of an early agreement with Gwynnes was that they provide and fix new axles and wheels to the tanks 'when required'. In 1905, the committee authorised a spare axle and set of wheels to be obtained from the manufacturers at a cost of £60. The reasons behind this are not enlarged upon. Company minutes give more detail of the spares situation.

the ability of his reservoirs to contribute to the main line water supplies if needed.

The hydraulic accumulator was situated in the boiler house, so the stoker would probably have had control over this as well. It may have had an automatic device so that when the ballast weight had reached the bottom of its travel a valve was actuated to bring in the duplex pump to recharge the accumulator.

The continual evaporation of steam from the boiler builds up the level of solids in the water. If canal water was used for boiler feed then the level of suspended solids would have been high to begin with. The boiler would be 'blown down' regularly to remove these solids. By opening a valve, water from the bottom of the boiler is blown out through a pipe. There is evidence that the blow down pit at Foxton was situated just outside the boiler house by the side ponds. As several gallons of water at around 100 psi were released suddenly to atmosphere, they would flash off into a great cloud of steam rising from the pit.

By all accounts, the Lift did not generate the increased traffic that was hoped for, so the engine driver's life may have been fairly quiet. At the start of a run, the condenser would not

pull vacuum immediately so the cut off would be adjusted to admit steam for a longer part of the stroke. The driver would also have to ensure that the link motion reversing gear was set correctly for the caissons to move in the required direction. As the tanks neared the end of their run, he would slow the engine and stop it at exactly the right spot, probably by aligning a mark on the winding drum with a fixed pointer. Engine houses of this period were usually kept spotless. With a permanent staff of three, there was no provision for a full-time cleaner so the driver may have done much of this work, perhaps working to a weekly timetable.

As Foxton was the Grand Junction Company prestige project, it would have been an ideal opportunity to install a steam-powered generator to light the site by electricity. However, it seems that the Lift was never run on a 24 hour basis so perhaps this is why oil lamps were used. Photographs clearly show one hanging in the engine room. No doubt the oil lamps in the boiler house gained a thick coating of coal dust and on a winter's afternoon, the gloom would have been pierced by a red glow when the fire doors were opened.

At the end of the day, the driver would shut

off the steam, open the cylinder drain cocks and wipe the engine over. The stoker would still have plenty to do to put the boiler to bed. He would see that the water level was well up in the gauge glass, give the bed a good rake to allow the ash and clinker to fall through the fire bars, throw on some more coal and bank up the fire at the back of the grate. The ash would be removed and barrowed out, possibly to be used later for resurfacing the towpath. There was no shower room to clean up in. The men might have had a wooden water tub which could be warmed up by sparging steam into it. Besides the day-to-day care of the plant, more major maintenance would have been required. Steam engines were built to last and most jobs could be tackled by a skilled fitter. Only one boiler was actually needed to run the plant. The system may have been to use one main duty boiler for a year, the other being worked on or acting as a standby. If a boiler became badly scaled inside some unfortunate person had the task of chipping it off. Having climbed inside a Lancashire's drum, I know that this must have been a hot, dirty, tiring, and claustrophobic job. The flue and chimney base would probably have had their accumulation of soot and ash removed yearly. The Foxton flue was quite short and I expect the cleaning took place during a stoppage. In some pumping stations where steam was needed 24 hours a day 365 days a year this job could be most unpleasant. The damper was shut right down to restrict the flow of hot gases, and the men wrapped wet sacking around their bodies, put scarves over their faces, went into the flue, and started shovelling! It is easy to be romantic about steam nowadays, but the reality of working conditions was a far cry from the nostalgic image.

Boiler Problems

David Heathcote's description - based on a practical experience of steam, and an intimate knowledge of the Foxton site, is uncannily accurate, although written without access to the Millner information. It is most interesting to compare Braunston again, where a picture of poor operating conditions, coupled with much heavier use than the Foxton engine would have had to endure, begins to emerge. Boiler feed water for the pump engine must have been drawn from the canal. Why some efficient means of filtering the water, if the canal had to be used, or the provision of a much better clean water system, was not made a priority is difficult to understand.

One can easily see from these few short anecdotes what working with steam really meant. If Foxton had survived, it would have been no different. In fact, more direct parallels can be drawn between the two sites.

If the Braunston chimney needed attention in 1925, maybe by 1927, the time the Foxton chimney was demolished, that was in need of maintenance too. Despite not being in regular use unused chimneys suffer from condensation and frost damage, often needing attention.

It has been said that the age of steam "bred a certain type of man". It would certainly have the effect of quickly knocking into shape, or breaking, the operators. If these quotes are anything to go by, the machinery could be temperamental and unforgiving if a regular pattern of careful planned maintenance was not strictly observed. This kind of work would have been echoed on thousands of other sites throughout the realm.

Lift Closure

One major problem with the Lift was that it was not manned at night, and therefore it was impossible to pass traffic after it had closed for the day. Fellows Morton & Clayton wanted to run 'fly' or fast boats on this route, which worked 24 hours a day, and this was a considerable hindrance to them.

Mainly for this reason, in 1908 £1,000 was set aside to put the lock flight, which had been allowed to deteriorate, back into proper order. Many blue bricks in the locks of 1909-10 indicate the progress of this work throughout the flight. The side pounds and passing pound were treated to a face-lift too. Stone revetment walls appearing where the Incline earthworks had part filled the original structures. The cost of the lock refurbishing and manning (with a night time lock-keeper) added to the site's upkeep. The maintenance of the Lift, wages for three men to operate it, and the cost of the locks, showed up a duplication of effort. It must have become obvious that the Lift's days were numbered.

Following the re-opening of the locks, there was a notable increase in trade but, due to the problems with water supply, this was a mixed blessing. In October 1910, the committee gave instructions for the Lift to cease working after a fortnight's notice "and the locks to be utilised." It was also declared that it was proposed that the canal be closed at night between Foxton and Leicester, but FMC naturally objected, and the Grand Junction Company said they would "delay such closing for a reasonable period to enable them to reorganise their working arrangements", promising discussions, "if desired".

No conclusions from this are recorded, but traffic fell substantially and these combined factors led to the final closure of the Lift in November 1910. In fact, there does not seem to have been an official closure - rather it was mothballed for possible future use (proof that it closed for economical rather than mechanical reasons). Although dates are recorded for opening and closure, in practice the Lift's active life seems to have been rather arbitrary, and it

The Pump House at Braunston under construction. Bottom left is the centrifugal pump, the boiler is on the right. The windows are in place waiting for the brickwork to go up round them. All windows and brick decoration are very close in design to Foxton.

worked on spasmodically into 1911, and afterwards on occasions when maintenance works closed the locks.

The Foxton boilers. On the left is the pump to feed the accumulator. It is unclear whether this is construction or demolition, however it is believed to be construction, and prior to the final floor being laid.

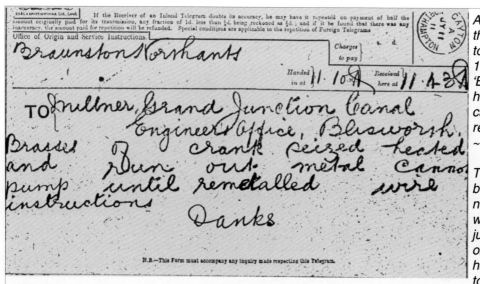

A telegram sent by Danks, the Braunston engine man, to Millner at Blisworth, July 11th 1911. He says, 'Brasses of crank seized heated and run out metal cannot pump until remetalled wire instructions ~ Danks'.

This means that the metal bearings in the pump needed replacing, which was a very skilled job, not just a matter of getting new ones and fitting them. They had to be adjusted by hand to fit exactly. Telegrams, often referred to as "a wire", were a means of passing 'faster than letter post' messages. The bare text (words cost money) was accepted at a post office, transmitted to a distant central office, and hand delivered by a boy!

Lock repairs 1909. The locks appear to be in a sad state. A crane is at work at the top lock, brickwork needs repair, a lock bridge is missing and the gates need painting if not replacing.

   A second building sits opposite the existing lock house. It has an external staircase and big windows. Was it a dwelling, or lock keeper's control box? Little trace of the building exists today.

FMC Steamer Phoenix with an all male crew was one of the boats used to on the London Nottingham 'fly run'.
This necessitated night use of the locks.

The locks around 1909 with the lift in the background. The gates, bridges, paddle gear and strapping post have all been painted white, possibly to help visibility for night working.

A portable steam engine driving a pump taking water from the bottom lock during a drought in the 1930s. A second engine was set up near the middle lock to boost the pressure. Operators used the steam whistle to communicate. They worked into the evenings.

Water Supply and Use

The 20-mile summit above Foxton has tunnels piercing the main watershed ridges. Beyond Crick tunnel, drainage is to the Nene. From Crick through to Husbands Bosworth tunnels the canal is in the catchment area of the Warwickshire Avon. From Bosworth to Foxton, water drains into the Welland. The Market Harborough level passes through Saddington tunnel. From here, the route is through the headwaters of the Soar catchment. Water runs to the summit from reservoirs constructed at Naseby, Sulby, and Welford; there are feeders directly into the canal at Welford (River Avon), Winwick, Elkington, Husbands Bosworth, Crick, and North Kilworth (given in order of volume). There are many smaller watercourses, which only run in wet weather.

Traffic through the locks uses large quantities of water - a wide lock contains some 56,000 gallons. Foxton's narrow locks take about 25,000 gallons per boat. The summit was constructed wide, the lock flights at Foxton and Watford were built narrow, possibly with the water supply in mind. There were other losses, and leaks of course, but evaporation from the water surface, transpiration through bank side vegetation - even the effect of cattle drinking entered the equation and had to be considered. In other areas, certainly in modern times, water abstraction for use in industry, principally power stations, and for irrigation of crops, are major factors which British Waterways and the water authorities have to monitor carefully, even on rivers.

In theory, water supplies would have been sufficient in an average year. In a drought, however, the Grand Junction Canal Company sacrificed summit water to keep traffic flowing on the more commercial main line (Birmingham to London) and water was run down at the Watford end. There have been occasions when back pumping from the Market Harborough level has been conducted with the aid of portable steam engines to drive pumps to lift the water up the Foxton flight. This enabled water from Saddington reservoir to be passed over the summit to the main line.

The Foxton Incline was set in an ideal location - it saved time and water. The original scheme included a complementary lift at Watford, which never materialised. Plans to complete the wide through route by rebuilding the Watford locks to 14 ft wide were also shelved, and the flight refurbished in 1902 to the original width. Plans were deposited again in the thirties for wide locks at both ends of the summit - they were never built.

The second pump being set up above the passing pound. The engine sits on the bank and the pump is mounted over the lock. It will be driven by an endless belt. Just getting the engine to this point would be heavy work involving a hand operated winch.

Ice breaking boat, now named 'Thomas Holt', in use during back pumping at Foxton.

Water Use

Regarding the use of water, calculations were done before the Incline was constructed, based upon the operation of wide boats, and comparing their use of water from the summit against passage through wide locks. The theoretical figures obtained were ideals - the boats used over the route were narrowboats. Maximum efficiency could only be achieved with high and constant traffic levels, something the promoters aimed for, but which was always to elude them on the Leicestershire waterways in the Lift era.

Each operation of the Lift would use the amount lost between the gates when docking (only one per cent of a wide lock full of water). A complete system with lifts at Foxton and Watford would consume very little water. It is worth noting that modern pleasure traffic probably makes as great a demand, or more, on water supply than at any time in the past. Demand is now mostly in the summer rather than being spread throughout the year. Lock-keepers help to maximise efficiency at lock flights such as Foxton and Watford.

Repairs and Maintenance

The expenditure accounts of an old canal company may seem dry reading, but sources such as this give the clearest picture of the daily chores that occupied company employees. The Foxton Lift was part of the Grand Junction empire, and would have represented the world of those proud Victorians in microcosm. Bricklayers, masons, carpenters, labourers, and blacksmiths would all be involved in the day-to-day maintenance long after construction was complete. Keeping paths and hedges in good order, clearing ponds and drains, jobs involving ropes, painting, tarring and oiling went on throughout the year. The Lift equipment, from engine and winding gear, the hauling and hydraulic systems, to the boilers and flues, would all need detailed specialist attention. Drought in summer, frost and ice in winter, all bringing their own particular problems.

Mention has been made of trouble with the rail timbers, a problem that has been rather over-emphasised in the past. Research indicates that the Incline rails had fewer holding bolts than was railway practice. Obviously the movement of a 240 ton tank at a fraction of one mile per hour on a 1:4 (25%) slope was a different proposition to the passages of an express train. The supporting baulks were probably of varying quality and 'poor' ones would have needed replacement. Certainly most have rotted away, but a few still survive on the site and one is preserved in the Museum. It appears that another major departure from railway design was the initial use of coach-type bolts screwed into the timber. Through-bolts, with keeper plates beneath, were a better design, and this was employed on the Incline at rail-ends.

Another view of the locks during the back pumping operation. It also shows the passing pound before part of it was filled in.

The Working Incline Recalled

The canal, locks and Lift must have made quite an impact on the local scene, both visually and in economic and social terms. Some of those involved recall life on the local canal at that time.

A staff of three was needed to run the lift, Tommy Mercer, Jess Holyland and John Cryer. One was in the boiler house, one at the top operating the engine and the guillotine gates, and one at the bottom of the Lift, again to operate the guillotine gates. The boiler, we are told, was adorned with a 'magnificent brass whistle' the main use of which was to let the engineer's wife know when he was coming home for his evening meal! A farmer's wife from Gumley sent sandwiches for lunch.

Mrs Dainty

Mrs Daisy Dainty recalled her life, extending back to the spring of 1909, when her father was offered the lock-keeper's job at Kibworth Top. This promotion, from canal lengthsman, meant a move for the entire household from Husbands Bosworth. This was undertaken by Company narrowboats and involved a trip down the Lift towards the end of its working days. The family possessions were taken by horse and cart from Bosworth to Kilworth Wharf, to be put aboard. The party arrived at Foxton about mid-day.

"The boat got into the side pond (upper arm) to go down. There were a pair of boats in the tank at the bottom, and so they hurried us in at the top. I can remember the big wheels with the wires around them, and the big chimney with smoke coming out of the top - the fire must have been going all right. I thought that when we went down the tank would tip and the water splash out. I think mother was afraid too, but we went gently down, the other tank passing us halfway; it took just over five minutes. The guillotine (gate) went up and we swam out into the side pond (bottom docks). The horse was hooked up, and pulled us round to the Kibworth Bridge. We had dinner at the bottom. I thought I was in a strange world below Foxton, having come down the big hill - father had talked of Kibworth, but we had never seen it."

Looking back at Mrs Dainty's life at Kibworth, it seems idyllic. The family kept chickens and their own pig, selling eggs and meat. But her father's wages were very low, and these enterprises were more necessities to make ends meet. Her mother did dressmaking, and Mrs Dainty as a young girl got a job with a local hosiery factory. A later occupant of the lock cottage remembers a piped water supply being installed in the 1950s, but Mrs Dainty's previous supply had to be carried from a spring in the field opposite the lock. The outdoor toilet was flushed by raising a paddle alongside the lock! Mains electricity was still to be connected.

Mrs Dainty remembers there were a few steam driven boats, which were a regular attraction. They were crewed by four men. Steamers are usually manned by three men, if on a fly run. If they had a Butty Boat they may have had two more crew, but six is unlikely. They kept going day and night. "I liked the steamers, they were clean, not like the motor boats which started in 1914 - they were really smelly to begin with." Life on board the working boats was hard, although she recalls, "Some of the cabins were like little palaces". She also tells of the tragic case of a young boy scalded to death when the boat nudged a bridge hole and a preparation of linseed oil, used as a rub for the horse, had been heating on the stove. There was the equally sad case of a girl sent lock wheeling ahead of the boats one winter. While raking the ice from behind a gate, she had missed her footing and fallen in. When the boats got to the spot, she was dead. Yet a third fatal accident involved another girl whose clothing caught alight on a camp-fire on the bank. The typical belt she wore around her waist to keep the windlass tucked in prevented her rescuers from removing her clothes in time.

Although her own life was hard, Mrs Dainty said it was a happy one. She remembered how as lock-keeper her father had to keep count of the boats going up and down, keep a tally on lock operations, and check the level of the top pound. All the information was posted to Canal Company offices each Sunday night. Part of his duties involved controlling the sluices at Saddington reservoir, a task he would have to fulfil in the middle of wet nights, to keep levels correct.

She tells an amusing anecdote of the time her father had locked the flight and left, in preparation for a stoppage nearer Leicester. Later, a violent tapping at the window revealed a boat waiting at the gates and the frantic captain insisting he must go on to Leicester. While she was explaining the situation, a telegram arrived - "PLEASE LET 'GUERNSEY' THROUGH" which she promptly did. The vital cargo, which could not wait? A boatload of bulldogs bound for the Abbey Park Show!

Percy Durran

Percy's father was involved with the construction of the Lift, being responsible for the wooden winding house. He lived further south originally, and came to Foxton for the Lift contract. As a boy, Percy lived in the cottage at the foot of the Foxton flight, starting work, aged 17, for the Grand Union Canal Company. He was an apprentice carpenter, working with his father. "Every winter for six winters I went up to Bulbourne, which was the headquarters for making lock gates, to get an insight into the building. I used to go off in October and come back in March, then work on the district with my father." When he married, Percy lived in Foxton village for four years and, when his father retired, he took over, eventually spending 25 years as District Foreman with responsibility for Grand Union waters.

"Head Office used to be in Belgrave Gate in Leicester; I used to go each day to my office at Kilby Bridge. I had four different managers over me in the 50 years I was on the canal. I used to set out work on the district - if there were complaints or inquiries, I used to visit the farmers and people along the canal. Cattle strayed through fences, water leaked through banks; when we got complaints I used to go and see these different jobs and then set the men on to do the work. When we had stoppages for new lock gates we used to work from four in the morning to eight at night - a day and a half! Labourers' wages at the time were 17 shillings (85p) per week, and the tradesmen 30 shillings (£1.50) - you had to be a good tradesman to get 30 shillings."

Tunnel repairs were carried out in the winter, they would work perhaps a month at a time, sleeping on the boats and only coming home at the weekends. "We all had to do that when we started. When I first started there were 50 to 60 pairs of boats through Foxton a week, they worked right through to the end of WWII when the trade went altogether from the canals - motor lorries took over." Percy referred to his retirement in terms which sum up the philosophy of a dedicated canal man, "I got to retiring age which was 65, I had done 48 years; they let me carry on for two years to make 50 years service, for which I was very pleased." Percy died in 1982.

Percy also recalled a few details of the Lift. The route of the old horse-path, now very difficult to trace on site, followed roughly around the outer boundary furthest from the locks. Coal to fire the boilers was unloaded at the top and fed by a chute to the coal store area. It was then barrowed inside to feed the boilers. When the Lift was dismantled, he was upset that the good tongue and groove woodwork from the boiler house should go to waste, so he salvaged it to panel out a room in the bottom lock house.

Percy remembered using the boat subsequently restored by the members of the Old Union Canals Society and renamed 'Gordon Thomas'. It was worth all the effort to see the look on Percy's face when he saw the boat after restoration - it was almost as if he was meeting with an old friend. He recalled journeys undertaken along the Harborough arm to Trenery's wood yard, at Market Harborough basin, pulled by a pony, and recounted making makeshift repairs to the hull by jamming matchsticks into pinholes as they appeared (a familiar problem to those involved with the restoration of this craft)! A second restored craft, an old icebreaker re-named 'Thomas Holt' is now on display on the Incline site along with 'Gordon Thomas'.

Gordon Thomas, Lift Engineer

Remembered by:
Miss G. M. Gilbert of Welford

Miss Gilbert lived at the end of the Welford Arm where her family ran several businesses. She was later to become the proprietor.

She took over the family boat business, which had been established in 1891 at Welford Wharf. Among reminiscences of the coal, lime and stone traffic she says: "I remember the late Mr Gordon Thomas and a Mr Bliss, they used to come here in a nice boat - one only saw that type on the River Thames in those days. They would ask my sister and me to have a ride as far as the locks. They had a man dressed in white, and when he tried to turn the boat in the turning hole, I remember so well, when he stuck the pole in to push it around, it stuck in the mud and he went down in the canal! As Mr Thomas said: "Well you haven't had a very long ride, but you have had jolly good laugh!"

Commenting on the canal scene today, Miss Gilbert concluded: "I cannot believe my eyes sometimes when I look out of the window. I wonder what they would all think if they could see the pleasure boats instead of coal boats, and a 1,000 tons (of coal) stacked in the yard. In those days men stayed in a job 45-50 years, and girls in the house until they got married. We live in a different world now."

Scrapping The Foxton Lift
Failed Negotiations

The GJCCo. business was normally conducted slickly enough. It seems that, in June 1924, Millner had mentioned to K.W. Williams, a director of Blackwell & Son of Northampton, that the GJC wished to sell the Lift. Blackwells were Engineers and Boilermakers in the town, at Cotton End, and said in their letter to Head Office, that they had a client who 'would purchase this if your Company are prepared to sell it for breaking up'. They added, 'the people we have in mind are a firm of repute'. This firm turned out to be Messrs. Cox & Danks Ltd. of Birmingham. The original Northampton letter had missed the June committee meeting of the canal company, so it was almost a month before a Mr. P.H. Humphries (of Cox & Danks) was writing to Millner direct. He asked for an appointment to inspect the Foxton Lift saying 'a day's notice and we will fit in to suit your own convenience', and assuring Millner he would 'quote you our own very best price'. Millner started negotiations with three canal

carriers - Faulkners, of Leighton, Griffiths of Bedworth, and the 'local' man- Charlie Woodhouse at Kilworth Wharf. This last mentioned carrier was used later on to move the scrap in 1928, but only as far as his Kilworth base, from where it was taken to the railway station.

The 1924 fiasco was only a rehearsal for the way things were to go from then on. In 1926, following another enquiry, a price of £250 was put on the engine and £175 for each of the boilers. Whether the scrap men consistently quoted too low (as in '24), or the company's expectations were too high (as in '26), it amounted to the same thing, and the Lift lingered on. By 1927, the company engineers were being told to send all scrap iron to Bulbourne. Perhaps this was really the heart of the Foxton matter - difficult site access, therefore no easy means of disposing of the materials, was the real bar to a successful sale.

In the end, Messrs. Glaze & Whorton of Wellington in Shropshire offered a paltry £250 for everything 'as and where it lies'. This meant everything - engine & boilers, tanks, aqueduct, hauling drums and wire ropes: the date was April 11th 1928. The Grand Junction era was itself drawing to a close, and the company was evidently making a desperate bid to be rid of the embarrassment the Lift must then have represented - at any price! It had been eighteen years since it was last in use. Millner, the last of the engineers from the Lift's time, was due to retire in a year or so, and the GJCCo to be handed over to the new Grand Union Canal Company.

Demolition

There are photographs in the Trust's collection of the chimney being demolished in 1927. Those who have seen the late Fred Dibnah, the Bolton Steeplejack, perform on television will understand the method employed. A section of brickwork around the back face was removed, and the chimney propped with timber. With more wood piled around, it was set alight. The photos show the flames licking round the base as the fire started to 'draw', and one last shot captures the moment when the props burnt through and the stack began to topple back across the Incline. The demolition of the chimney (the bricks were reused for general canal repairs) was the beginning of the end for the Inclined Plane.

Once the decision was taken to accept a tender, demolition proper was swift, using methods that would still be employed today. The most valuable and easily removed items would go first; the steam engine was probably new in the first place, and this could readily be serviced and sold on elsewhere. Other items with some resale value would follow - the winding gear and hauling cables. All the various hydraulics - rams, valves, pumps, etc, the chains and pulleys of the gate operating mechanisms would be saved, some of these possibly being kept by the Company for its own use. Certainly the Lift's mooring bollards appeared alongside the flight, and can still be seen today. The windows and doors from the boiler house were taken to Tring Pump in 1927 to furnish an extension when the original beam engines and pumps were replaced. Mention has already been made of the re-use of bricks. Larger items, such as stone copings, seem to have been left on site - awkward to move and of limited use. When it came to the metal items, the non-ferrous materials would be sought out. There would have been many bronze bearings, copper and brass fittings.

The bulk of the metal was iron, and most of this came from the aqueduct and the tanks themselves. Securely propped on the slopes, these old fabrications would have to be cut up piecemeal, using oxy-acetylene. Track bolts would be similarly dealt with. Rail items would be smashed out and loaded into boats waiting below.

One of the boats was the Margaret, belonging to the Charlie Woodhouse family, who operated from North Kilworth. She was left loaded, and broke her back. Her cargo was transhipped. The wreck stayed there for the next 40 years. The old boilers would pose transport difficulties, and it is possible that such big items would also have been scrapped along with many of the other specially made items, wheels, etc. used in the old constructions.

It appears that an attempt was made to recover parts of the underground structure work, detaching them by the use of explosives. There are otherwise unexplained holes at the site of the buffer-stops' legs, and a gully in the bank around two of the main bearing pits. As these are the only places however, the exercise was obviously difficult and unprofitable and it was not followed systematically all over the site. In the end, the scrap men had to be satisfied with cutting through just below ground level. Likewise, no attempt seems to have been made to de-water the lower dock and to get pulley wheels, etc. When the water was removed, to facilitate bridge repairs in the 1980s, they were still in place, and one was removed for display on the bank above the bottom dock. It now rests in the new car park.

Of the demolition, as with any modern building site, the scene would have been one of dereliction and waste. The once grand structure was reduced to a meaningless jumble of metal with building rubble scattered about. Unwanted timber would be burnt, the smoke from the fires drifting about and adding to the air of desolation. Nature would swiftly take over: weeds and scrub at first, then ash and hawthorn producing the jungle of recent memory.

The site was to be left to rabbits and children, neither knowing nor caring about the significance of the remains. The site was to sleep on for 40 years before our industrial heritage became an acceptable and, indeed, popular subject for study.

Left

The chimney was the first to go. Brickwork at the base was removed and the chimney propped up on timber. This was then burned, just like Fred Dibnah did it.

The coping stones in the wall behind the chimney were damaged in the process and this can still be seen today. The chimney base complete with lightning conductor has been rebuilt.

Right

The windows have gone to Tring, and the demolition men seem to be posing for the camera, perhaps the finial from the top of the accumulator building is the next thing to go?

Demolition or construction? It's difficult to tell but either way the winding drum was probably the most solid item to deal with. This shot shows that it wasn't just a plain drum. The rope followed a groove, a bit like a screw thread. This would prevent the rope running over itself which would change its length to the tank.

Local men view the partially demolished remains of the tanks. The boat to carry it away can be seen at the bottom of the hill. The flat metal plates have been removed first. These could possibly have been reused.

Foxton Inclined Plane Trust

The History

The Foxton Inclined Plane Society was formed in 1979 as the result of a meeting called by Dr Frank Foden of The Council for the Protection of Rural England. Dr Foden and Peter Gardener wrote the first authoritative booklet on the lift. The CPRE had become interested in the Inclined Plane a couple of years earlier. They arranged for its listing as an ancient monument to protect its future, and organised work parties to clear part of the slope (the locks are also listed as grade 2*). Physical work was not in the CPRE brief and Dr Foden was leaving for an extended world cruise, so they decided to call a meeting, in Leicester, with the intention of forming a society to look after the Lift at Foxton. A couple of meetings, some debate about the aims and name, and the Foxton Inclined Plane Society (FIPS for short) was born. A few meetings later, the name was changed from Society to Trust, and the road to becoming an accepted charity started. Incorporated in 1980, FIPT was up and running.

It was a slow and often frustrating business getting people to take our stated aim of full restoration seriously. They called us the flat earth society and many believed that we were wasting our time. The demise of the Anderton Boat lift didn't help. Even some of our supporters believed that Anderton should be restored first. By then we had cleared the upper third of the incline, and made headway with the clearance of the upper canal arm to the lift. The best news so far came from a study of the lift by Alan Parker who, with the support of his Leicester University mentors, found that the lift foundations were in fair condition, and had not moved since it was constructed.

The Trust needed an on-site project that proved that it could deliver on its promises. This we did by reconstructing the boiler house using entirely voluntary labour. Work was spread over several years, with volunteers working every other weekend. One man, David Goodwin, worked on site nearly every day, laying a few bricks at a time, and talking to visitors about the project. One visitor, walking the canals for a holiday and camping under bridges at night, got so interested that he joined in for a few weeks. He was a professional bricklayer, known to all as ' Mick the Brick ', he continued working until we ran out of materials. Money for materials was raised in all of the usual ways, but the most effective was to sell a brick to visitors for £1 on which they wrote their names in felt tip pens, the bricks being built into the walls name facing inwards. Mrs Daisy Dainty and Ken Goodwin opened the building to the public as the Foxton Canal Museum on June 10th 1989. Ken as chairman of the IWA and Mrs Dainty the final person known to have ridden on the lift. She had, as a child, lived in Husbands Bosworth where she had helped raise the money for the Baptist chapel. The chapel was demolished and it's windows re-used in the

Mrs Daisy Dainty and Ken Goodwin cut the cake at the opening party for the museum in 1989.

museum. The Museum is now well established, employing two people and supported by a dedicated band of volunteers. The Museum is Accredited as a Museum with The MLA (Museums, Libraries and Archives Commission). The Trust continues to run regular work parties. Essex Waterways Recovery Group run weekend work parties at least twice a year. People of all ages continue working together to make the site better for everyone. Fund raising events at Foxton, and at various waterway festivals, form the backbone of our efforts to raise money in support of the restoration.

Feasible and Sustainable

The next big step was the formation of the Foxton Locks Partnership, and the commissioning of the first professional feasibility study, the Atkins Report, in 2000. This said that the restoration was feasible and sustainable. It could be rebuilt on the same site, and that a combination of modest fees for its use, entrance fees to a visitor centre, and a trip boat for the public, would pay for operation and maintenance. The estimate for full restoration came out at £8m. This included a new visitor centre. Due to inflation this was subsequently increased to between £10m and £15m.

Things looked even more exciting when, in 2000, British Waterways announced that we would be one of a set of restoration projects and new waterways that would be promoted and helped by them. Flat Earth Society no more, FIPT was in at the top. The lift would get the attention it deserves.

The project was split into manageable chunks, partly due to the availability of Lottery funds. In the short term the Lottery could not undertake to finance the entire restoration in one go. Since then, it has been a roller-coaster ride, up one minute down the next. But with a lot of hard work by all concerned, a lot of debate about how to achieve our goals, things started to look really good when, in 2003, the first Lottery bid was submitted, and BW acquired the access it needed to build the kind of public facilities it thought necessary.

Some of this proved controversial, and will be debated for some time to come, but, over the winter of 2003/4, work started on site. A new access road to the bottom of the locks, removing vehicles from the old bridleway, has been completed. The old Bridge 61 pub has been taken over by BW and refurbished. The shop belonging to Foxton Boat Services was moved to the old stables adjacent to the bottom lock and the new 'Bridge 61' pub constructed next door. The top lock cottage and stables have been restored to their 1900 appearance. Excluding the developments of the pubs, over a million pounds was spent on this stage of the site restoration.

Main picture, the Top Cottage had suffered from inappropriate "modernisation" over the years and several years of neglect. It was restored in early 2004 to its 1900 appearance. Compare this with the picture on page 11.

Left, the scaffolding goes up on the semi derelict cottage.

Foxton Locks Inn, formerly Bridge 61, refurbishment works nearly complete. The inn is a relatively formal restaurant establishment which has become very popular in the summer. Compare this with the picture on page 11.

The new version of Bridge 61, photographed in the snow shortly after opening in 2006. This is an intimate traditional pub specialising in simple pub grub.

Three Years of Restoration

In 2008 we saw the completion of three years of restoration at a cost of over three million pounds. The money came from £1.2m Heritage Lottery grant, the balance being raised by the Partnership. Grants were made by East Midlands Development Agency and Foxton Locks Partnership, which includes funds from British Waterways, Harborough District Council, The Welland Partnership and, of course, FIPT.

The intention was a Phase One restoration of the site and a big step towards the restoration/reconstruction of the Lift. The Lift was on the English Heritage Buildings At Risk Register, mainly due to the trees, the roots of which were destroying the Lift foundations. The site had become neglected over the years and visitor expectation has grown considerably. What was considered good twenty years ago is now unacceptable. As a result visitor numbers had declined and British Waterways wanted to make Foxton a flagship tourist destination. The FIPT wanted the lift to be restored to full working order, and considered this to be an important stepping stone towards the fulfilment of this goal.

The project was very diverse. It included big improvements to the visitor infrastructure, in particular access for visitors with disabilities, including those who need to use a wheelchair. A swing bridge over the Harborough arm providing level access across the canal was part of this and part of the planning permission for the works to the Foxton Locks Inn. The trees were to be removed from the Incline and more planted elsewhere to compensate nature for their loss. The bottom dock of the Incline, used for years as a mooring basin, was to be cleaned out and its walls repaired. The upper canal leading to the Lift, dry since 1928, was to be restored and rewatered. The final works would provide interpretation for site visitors. The following illustrations and their captions give a more detailed picture of the works undertaken. They are organised in sections where the works could be grouped together rather than in chronological order.

Trees

The bottom half of the Incline was covered in trees, some as much as 80 years old, but most of a very weedy nature as they were self seeded and growing in concrete or compacted clay. Some had fallen due to poor root structure and torn holes in the concrete rail foundations. All of them were tangled up with ivy. Volunteers from Waterways Recovery Group were drafted in to do the work. Essex Branch of WRG have been long term supporters of the Foxton project, visiting the site at least twice a year. They cleared some of the lower branches and scrub to make way for the WRG Forestry Team, all volunteers, but trained in the art of tree surgery. They came from all over the country. The work was planned for completion in a week, with the help of volunteers from lots of organisations to remove the cut material. The volunteers camped out in the Robert Monk Hall in Foxton Village. In reality, it was to take a couple of weeks and a couple of weekends. Due to the difficulties caused by the ivy which was choking the wood, and tying it together at high level, and the difficulties of carrying the cut material up a 1:4 incline covered in small stumps and pot holes. The latter was improved when WRG were given permission to use tracked mechanical equipment, in the form of a tipper truck and tracked chipper, so that the chipper could go to the material rather than the material going to the chipper.

The small material was chipped for use as mulch around the base of the replacement trees. The bigger material was sold as logs for firewood.

Using a chainsaw up a tree is a high-risk skilled occupation. These volunteers have done all of the necessary training.

Volunteers rig an aerial ropeway to help move materials from the lower part of the Incline.

Above, One half of the Incline is nearly clear. The chipper is in use at the bottom and the tracked dumper is being used to remove the logs. The second slope is still covered in trees and gives an indication of the size of the job.

Right, The last and biggest tree.

Mitigation

Around 60 trees and various areas of scrub were removed and as mitigation 2500 trees and hedging plants were planted mainly alongside the new access road.

This was done mostly by volunteers, including parties from various local schools. Some children were enthusiastically getting their hands dirty while others wouldn't take their woolly gloves off! It was, however, a success because around 120 children now have ownership of our trees. Whilst on site they were treated to a tour which included a talk about being safe by water. Each school planted one of the big trees.

A couple of days were set aside for members of the public to plant the hedges which they did zealously.

A VIP planting was also arranged for the press, (picture on the right). On the left is Project Manager James Clifton of British Waterways. Next is FIPT President, David Stevenson, FIPT Company Secretary and Museum Keeper, Mike Beech (planting a beech tree). To the right of the tree is FIPT Vice Chairman, Bill Manton, and on the far right is BW Conservation Officer, Peter Chowns. Our MP Edward Garnier and MEP Roger Helmer also planted a tree and have officially visited Foxton on several occasions.

Bottom basin

The bottom basin was for many years just a backwater off-line mooring for Foxton Boat Services. With doubt about its future use, maintenance was minimal and it had got into a rather sad state. The tree growth on the Incline concealed its real purpose and most visitors hadn't a clue that it was something far more exciting than just another mooring. Over the years it had silted up and trees had grown through the waterway walls. At some point in the past, probably in the 1930s refurbishment, most of the copings had been removed for reuse on the lock sides. When Foxton Boat Services set up their moorings in the 1960s no-one was interested in this surplus piece of water.

The first and biggest task was the dredging of the basin. This was done in two stages. At first a fabric dam was placed across the entrance and the water pumped out. Next, a steep access ramp was constructed and large diggers went into the bottom of the dock and excavated the mud, passing it back to a long-reach excavator on the top of the bank. The silt removed from the canal was screened and spread a few inches thick on a nearby field. With this work completed it was possible to survey the dock and estimate the work needed to restore it. This included a survey to inform English Heritage in order to gain the necessary permission for works on a grade one listed structure. The water was then returned and the moorers let back in for a few months. The next stage was completed when the main contractors arrived. A more permanent dam was built with a ramp into the bottom to allow dump trucks and other machinery easy access. Mud or silt had flowed like water back into the bottom dock from the main canal and this had to be removed before the walls were reconstructed. The pier separating the docks was restored using green oak, mounted on the remains of the original. Work was going well until the contractors removed the remains of an old wall, and the land behind

it, slipped into the channel. This was not part of the Inclined Plane, but clearing it away and putting in a new reinforced wall was expensive and time consuming. Several months passed whilst permission was sought from English Heritage. Meanwhile the residential moorers who had vacated the dock for the duration of the works were left over winter on temporary moorings. They were not happy. This was the only incident to delay the entire project which otherwise came in on time and, even with this disaster, on budget. With the work completed boaters returned to a posh new mooring and the public had access to the basin for the first time.

Above, viewed from the bridge, some of the mud has been removed. At first it was above the tracks of the digger. The access ramp can be seen in the background.

Left, viewed from the Incline a pair of excavators work, passing material from one to another. A third machine then moved it to the bottom of the ramp for final removal. Also visible are the old landing stages for the boats and down the centre, the remains of the pier.

Left, the bank which had slipped during repairs. The tops of the reinforcing piles can be seen.

Below, final touches are made to the waterway walls, and the copings set in place.

Below, water and boats back in. In the foreground is the top of the new pier. The original can be seen on page 39. Under water is a complex structure of large oak timbers, strong enough for the boats to hit it and the tanks to push up to it. On the bank on the left you can see one of the new facilities posts which give boaters electricity, water and the possibility of a telephone connection.
A floating link gives public access to the pier.

Work on the top arm was the biggest of the engineering works. It had been undermined by badgers, and the first job was to build them a new home nearby, and, over several weeks, persuade them to move. Then the arm was cleaned out to its original profile, plus a bit more to allow for the new lining. Heavy duty (see above) steel piling one and a half times the height of a double-decker bus was driven in along the centre line of the tow path. If the badgers come back they won't be able to cause disaster. The channel was then lined with a high tech plastic pond liner, the joints being welded together. This was protected with a white fleece before the bottom was covered in a protective layer of concrete. The sides were protected with interlocking concrete blocks which allow pockets where small plants can get a foothold. At the top of the bank a shallow wall of concrete blocks was constructed for a pocket behind

which reeds and other aquatic plants can thrive. English Heritage would not allow the banks to be made vertical, and therefore convenient for the mooring of boats, because it had to be restored to the original profile.

At the southern end of the section, furthest from the Lift, the original stop gate structure had to be restored. This time it was volunteers from British Waterways who restored the brickwork, (see picture at the bottom of previous page) which had survived very well. This was the point at which the canal was dammed in 1928 and the soil infill had protected the structure. Only the top two or three brick courses had been exposed to the weather and small trees had grown in them. The new lock gates were paid for by a grant from the John Hobley Trust. John was the owner of a Leicester engineering company, whose will set up a trust which benefitted other charities involved with engineering works in the county.

At the Lift end of the arm a new dam was built with a

modern bridge over it to give access to the tow path. This matches the new observation platform added to the end of the tow path giving a bird's eye view of the Incline and the surrounding countryside.

Top, the new gates are fitted. It is unusual to have the luxury of a digger in the bottom of the canal to act as a crane for the gates. Whilst most of the works were carried out by contractors Morrison Construction, the fitting of the gates was undertaken by BW staff.

Bottom, the water runs in for the first time, watched by the TV cameras. The man operating the paddle is James Clifton of BW, and Chairman of Foxton Locks Partnership.

The new bridge and the dam (pictured above). Only weeks after the re-watering, the fish, including a large pike, had already colonised the arm, and plants which were not placed by human hand gradually appeared. Nature rapidly healed the scars and it was soon difficult to remember the disruption caused by the works.

Viewed from the Incline, the new observation platform is a popular addition to the site. The design mimics that of the pulley wheels for the Lift but as it is constructed in galvanised steel with stainless steel rope fencing it is definitely modern so that there can be no doubt that it isn't part of the original structure. In the centre of its base a bronze 'diorama' indicates the position of local places and famous waterway connections, including the Falkirk Wheel, London Docks and the Anderton Boat Lift.

Access Improvements

Wherever possible without spoiling the historic site, all paths have been improved and re-graded to ease the slope and resurfaced with a resin based material which binds the granite chips together. This makes it resistant to water erosion and gives a smooth surface with a good grip, whilst still looking like a gravel path. Some new paths have been introduced to give alternative access for wheelchair users, where it is inappropriate to change the look of the site. As their contribution to the lottery match funding Leicestershire County Council gave the large long-stay car park on the Gumley Road to British Waterways. The paths from it have also been resurfaced. The toilet block in the top car park was given a face lift and a new block added in the bottom car park. This provided facilities for boaters, rubbish disposal as well as more toilets. The new bottom short-stay car park is very popular despite the long-stay top car park being cheaper. The best approach to the site remains that from the top car park. You walk down the towpath and the spectacular sight of the locks descending the hill is backed by some of the best of our countryside.

New Swing Bridge

The new bridge being lowered into place at the entrance to the Harborough arm can be considered as a replacement because the original was put in to allow horses to get from the main canal across to the bottom dock of the Incline. Most of the boats using the Lift were horse-drawn, so it would have been well used. New swing bridges are a rarity because of the potential for accidents to pedestrians and disasters for boats. This one is fitted with a locking mechanism to prevent unauthorised movement of the bridge. The design is similar to the original although the new one is wider and the rails at the side are higher. Many people said that it would cause problems for boaters. Most of them seem to cope fine but we have witnessed some frustrating delays when the bridge doesn't seem to cooperate. The pedestrian visitors think it's wonderful.

The Incline

Cleared of trees and tidied up, the inclined plane slope of the boat lift has never looked better. For the first time since the formation of the FIPT you can stand at the top and see the boats at the bottom. It is now much easier to understand how it worked and how impressive it was.

Interpretation

The final part of the project was the installation of "interpretation" all over the site. Ranging from introductory 'entrance' information in car parks through bronze plates detailing the history of the buildings, to interpretation panels and statues. A sound tour is available for download from www.foxtonlocks.com or www.fipt.org.uk. In the top lock cottage, next to a statue of Jack Cryer one of the old lock keepers, there is a listening post, so that you can hear his story.

Introductory display in the long-stay Gumley Road car park

The new swing bridge in place.

Horse and boy on the tow path give an indication of canal life in the 1900s.

Interpretation panel showing how turnover bridges work. This is cast in bronze and securely mounted on green oak

In the observation platform a new topograph sets Foxton in its geographical context.

Left, the statue of Jack Cryer waiting for installation.

The Future

The intention of the first phase of the works was to leave the site looking good and in a sustainable position. It has moved the restoration on substantially but, even before the works were complete, the Partnership had started the process of finding money for the next batch of surveys and studies. These will ascertain the financial stability of a restored Incline and then assemble a bid to the Heritage Lottery Fund for a development grant. This process will take time to complete but we will be asking for a share of around £11m, and the paperwork must be complete and extensive. The price includes the entire infrastructure which may be needed to cope with extra visitors, such as more toilets, parking and perhaps changes to the local road system to protect Foxton village from excess traffic. Normally the Heritage Lottery Fund grant about 65% of the total estimated cost, so the Partnership will have to find the balance. FIPT has started fund raising for it's share of the development bid (all contributions appreciated!). Profits from this publication will help fund the Museum which in turn helps to fund the project. All donations above the entry fee go directly towards restoration. The Museum also provides a venue from which our volunteers run several fund raising events each year.

Seven Reasons to Restore the Lift

If you have read the rest of this book you must by now be convinced of the historic significance of the site, but why reconstruct the lift?

1.   A restored Incline would give Britain its only working Inclined Plane boat lift

Working boat lifts do exist in Britain. The vertical lift at Anderton in Cheshire was restored with Lottery and European money, and at Falkirk, near Edinburgh, the world's only wheel lift has been become one of Scotland's premier visitor attractions. The only other type of lift is the incline. Britain was acknowledged as world leader in boat lift technology, inspiring the design of lifts all over the world.

2. A restored lift would celebrate the achievements of British engineers and inspire engineers of the future.

3.   A restored lift would save water

When the lift was working the volume of waterway traffic was static. It was fighting the challenge posed by modern rail transport and improved roads, with early lorries taking some of the short distance trade. The Lift needed an increase to make it viable. Modern boat traffic is growing, and is concentrated in the summer months when water supply is at its lowest. In times of drought the canal has come close to closure. In 1976 it was closed for several months. Forecasts of more droughts are a regular feature on the news. Locks need 25,000 gallons of water per boat; the lift uses a tiny fraction of this. Yes it is true that the canal at the bottom of the lift needs water, but the supply could be controlled instead of fluctuating as traffic increases or decreases.

4.   A restored Lift will speed up the traffic and take the pressure off the overworked locks

On weekends and Bank Holidays, up to 50 boats a day try to squeeze through the Foxton bottleneck. This can cause delays of up to 5 hours, a substantial chunk of a long weekend's boating. Each boat taking a minimum of 45 minutes to negotiate the flight. The lift will move 2 up and 2 down in 12 minutes, including loading, and it would take visitors on a trip boat.

5.   A restored Lift would bring jobs to the area.

The south Leicestershire countryside is a great place to live, but it is turning into a commuter belt for those travelling to Leicester and London to work. Local jobs in the tourist industry are very important, and visitors to the Lift can be encouraged to stay for holidays in local hotels, spending money in local shops and pubs. Jobs on site will also be created in the visitor centre, at the Museum and in the pubs, cafes or shops. It will also need local people to maintain and run the Lift.

6   A restored Lift will help open up the canal system to wider boats.

Many boats are slightly too wide for the locks. Some barges are between 10 and 13 feet wide, and there is a growing trend for the use of converted barges, or replica barges especially, to live on. A restored lift would extend their cruising range, and, with a new lift or wide locks at Watford Gap, provide an opportunity to make the wide-beam north-south link which was the original plan of the Grand Junction Company.

7.   A restored Lift would revitalise the entire Leicester section of the Grand Union

The Leicester line is one of the country's waterways gems, and yet apart from a few 'honey pots' it is badly underused. It provides a link with the Rivers Soar and Trent. A working lift at Foxton would encourage boats to use the entire line of the canal, with crews spending their money in local shops and pubs along the whole line. More boats equals better maintenance and an improvement in the health of the waterway.

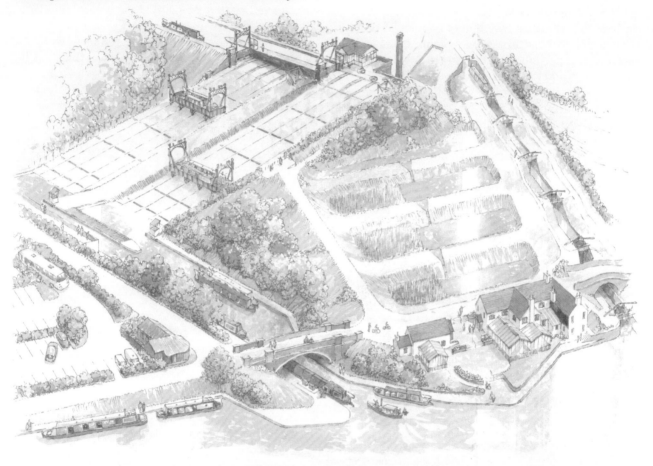

Above, an artist's impression of a restored inclined plane. This was drawn by one of our members, Mike Moore, before Foxton Locks Inn was built so it is slightly different in detail. Although a new lift would look like the original, it will probably run on electricity and be controlled by a computer - but this would all be hidden away. There is a possibility of steam for special weekends but we will have to wait for the engineering study to decide on that kind of detail.

Foxton Waterway Festival 2008

The final fling of the first stage of restoration was a festival to celebrate the works. It was held on the weekend closest to June 10th to commemorate the original opening of the lift in 1900. The weather was fantastic, possibly the best weekend of the year. It was the biggest event of its kind ever held at Foxton with several historic boats, including steam boat President and her butty Kildare. Actors played the part of characters from the past, and engineers gave conducted site tours. Various craft stalls, games, and charity stalls were spaced around the site. A display of live owls sat in a shady spot on the top of the Inclined Plane. Wigston Town Junior Brass Band and several folk singers added to the festive spirit.

The weekend started with the official opening of the works when Emma Sayer of the National Lottery Fund cut a ribbon stretched over the new bridge at the end of the top lift arm. British Waterways Chief Executive Robin Evans and MEP Roger Helmer were in attendance along with BW's James Clifton, the Foxton Locks Partnership Chairman, and other members of the Partnership and representatives of the various contractors.

The arrival of President and the other historic boats had created a lot of interest on the preceding Friday. President and her butty descending the locks attracted a good crowd. (A lucky few watched her go back up the flight on the Monday after.) Visitors to the event were encouraged to climb aboard the boats and find out how the crews lived and how the boats worked.

On the top of the Inclined Plane several performances of a specially commissioned play were performed by Andrew Ashwell associates. The play told the story of the Lift's construction with a bit of humour. The audience sat around on a few benches and on the grass. Historic boats were stationed on all approaches to the locks. President and Kildare took prime position at the bottom of the Incline, moored where their sister boats sat at the beginning of the last century. The basin was a fine sight with all of the boats dressed with colourful flags.

Foxton Canal Museum opened its doors free to all visitors, something FIPT cannot normally do because the entry fee pays the cost of running the Museum, and because it was swamped by the number of visitors.

Apart from a modest car park fee of just £1.50, the whole event was free.

Visitors expressed their pleasure at the condition of the site and its interpretation, and we received many compliments. The most treasured of these came from Mavis Bird who wrote to the Harborough Mail: "On behalf of family members, may I thank all who organised the Foxton Festival weekend. The wall plaque and statue at the top lock cottage of our Great-Grandfather John "Jack" Cryer was very much appreciated by us all. A fitting memorial to his working life as lock keeper at Foxton".

WRG volunteers help with finishing touches to the site before the event.

Steam boat President arrives at Foxton Top Lock for the Festival.

Left, volunteers on the FIPT fund raising stand at the Festival.

Left is BW Chief Executive Robin Evans. Right is MEP Roger Helmer. Emma Sayer of The National Lottery Fund cuts the ribbon. Behind Roger is BW's James Clifton, Partnership Chairman, along with other members of the Partnership. They are cutting the ribbon to formally celebrate the completion of the lottery project and to open the Festival.

Visitors crowd round the upper half of the locks at the beginning of the Festival. Gazebos are set up for some of the charity stalls.

The Partnership stand at the Festival. Essex Waterways Recovery Group were also in the tent.

Foxton Locks Partnership

Not just narrowboats, a couple of early pleasure boats also attended. This one, 'UNUS', was converted in the 1960s from an open boat previously used as a trip boat on the Trent. It is believed to date from the 1940s.

Owls proved a popular attraction. 'Chalkey' breeds the owls and takes them out to various events to meet the public.

Looking up the Incline Plane with President in the foreground and the duty engineer looking out. Kildare is the other side. In the next picture you can see Kildare, President's 'butty'. The boats are sitting where the tanks for the Incline would have been if they were going up the hill. This is the first time that boats contemporary with the Lift have been able to get to this point, and the first time they could be viewed from above, for a very long time.

Time Line

1793	Grand Junction Canal, between London and Braunston on the Oxford canal, commenced construction.
1793	The Leicestershire & Northamptonshire Union Canal (LNU) was also started. (Act of Parliament, 30 April 1793.)
1797	7 April - LNU temporarily halted at Debdale near Gumley.
1809	13 October LNU completed to Market Harborough on a revised route.
1810	A new company, the Grand Union Canal Company GUCCo came into existence .
1814	9 August - GUCCo opened including Foxton Locks from the bottom of the locks to Norton Junction, near Daventry. The Welford arm opened 3 months later.
1894	The Grand Junction Canal Company bought out the Leicestershire and Northamptonshire Union, for £6,500, and the Old Grand Union canal, for £10,500.
1894	The job of toll keeper at Foxton was abolished.
1896	Large scale model of Lift constructed at Bulbourne near Tring.
1900	The Lift opens for traffic.
1909	The Locks are refurbished for night use.
1911	The Lift is mothballed to save money. The GJCCo intend to reopen when things get better.
1914 - 1918	The canals come under government control and the Lift can't be scrapped in case it is needed for the war effort.
1927	Between 1927 and 1928 the Lift is scrapped.
1929	(*new*) Grand Union Canal Company formed, amalgamating the GJCCo and other canals.
1948	1st January. Most of the canal system was nationalised. Traffic falls because of better road transport. Factories start to convert from coal to electricity for power, as coal mines adjacent to several canals are closed
1950	The first ever Inland Festival of Boats is held in Market Harborough to promote the retention and use of the canals.
1968	Transport Act classified canals into three categories: Commercial, Cruiseway and Remainder, the Remainder to be treated in the most economical way (e.g. abandoned).
1980	The use of canals for leisure is established and the Incline Plane Trust is formed.
1989	Foxton Canal Museum opens.
2008	First stage of restoration is complete.

Conversion Table

	Imperial	Metric
Narrowboat and lock width (in reality just under)	7 ft	2.1 m
Wide lock or barge (usually just over)	14 ft	4.2 m
Length of lock or boat usually quoted as 70 ft but normally the boat is 72 ft and the lock long enough to accommodate it	72 ft	21 m
Difference between top and bottom of the locks or lift	75 ft 2 in	22 m